CW00382853

EDITED BY MIKE ROYSTON

WAYS WITH
WORDS

A NEW WINDMILL BOOK OF SHORT STORIES

Heinemann
New Windmills

Heinemann Educational Publishers
Halley Court, Jordan Hill, Oxford OX2 8EJ
A division of Reed Educational and Professional Publishing Ltd

OXFORD MELBOURNE AUCKLAND
JOHANNESBURG BLANTYRE GABORONE
IBADAN PORTSMOUTH (NH) USA CHICAGO

04 03 02 01 00
10 9 8 7 6 5 4 3 2 1

ISBN 0 435 12536 2

Acknowledgements

The publishers gratefully acknowledge the following for permission to reproduce copyright material.
Every effort has been made to trace copyright holders, but in some cases this has proved impossible.
The publishers would be happy to hear from any copyright holder that has not been acknowledged.

'Handsel And Gristle' by Michael Rosen from *Hairy Tales and Nursery Crimes,* published by Scholastic
Ltd, reprinted by permission of Scholastic Ltd. 'Getting Dead' by William F Nolan © 1991 by William F
Nolan, reprinted by permission of the author. 'Frankenstein's Hamster' by Barbara Griffiths, published
by All Books for Children 1990, reprinted by permission of HiT Entertainment Plc; 'A Straight Bat' by
Roger Holt, from *Smithereens* edited by R. Baines, published by Oxford University Press, Australia,
reprinted with permission of Richard Baines. 'The Trout' by Sean O'Faolain, © Sean O'Faolain 1947,
reproduced by permission of the Estate of Sean O'Faolain c/o Rogers, Coleridge & White Ltd, 20 Powis
Mews, London W11 1JN; 'The Flowers' by Alice Walker, from *The Complete Stories,* published by The
Women's Press, reprinted by permission of David Higham Associates Ltd. 'The Empty Box' by Johanna
Hurwitz, from *Birthday Surprises,* published by Morrow Junior Books USA © 1995 by Johanna Hurwitz,
reprinted by permission of HarperCollins Publishers Inc. `Do You Dance?' By Laurence Staig, from *The
Young Oxford Book of Supernatural Stories,* edited by Dennis Pepper, 1996, reprinted by permission of
the author. 'Out of the Everywhere' by Marilyn Watts, from *The Young Oxford Book of Aliens,* edited by
Dennis Pepper © Marilyn Watts 1998, reprinted with permission of the author. 'Fabric Crafts' by Anne
Fine, from *Families* edited by Miriam Hodgson, published by Egmont Children's Books, reprinted with
permission of David Higham Associates Ltd. 'Hobbyist' by Fredric Brown; copyright by the Estate of
Fredric Brown, reprinted by permission of the Estate and its agents, Scott Meredith Literary Agency, LP.
'A Price to Pay' by Timothy Callender from *It So Happens,* published by Heinemann Educational,
reprinted with permission of REPP. 'The Wasteland' by Alan Paton, from *Debbie Go Home,* published by
Jonathan Cape, reprinted by permission of The Random House Group Ltd. 'The Moonpath' by Robert
Swindells, reprinted with permission of Jennifer Luithlen Agency.

Cover illustration by John Leigh
Cover design by The Point
Typeset by 📐 Tek-Art, Croydon, Surrey
Printed and bound in the United Kingdom by Clays Ltd, St Ives plc

Tel: 01865 888058 www.heinemann.co.uk

Illustrations by Jackie Hill at 320 Design; 'Getting Dead' – John Holder; 'Many Happy Returns!' – John
Holder; 'The Trout' – Hashim Akib; 'Do You Dance?' – Hashim Akib; 'Fabric Crafts' – Tony Watson; 'A
Price to Pay' – Hashim Akib; 'The Princess Who Stood On Her Own Feet' – David Hopkins; 'The
Moonpath' – Hashim Akib

Contents

Introduction for Students   iv

Introduction for Teachers   v

Handsel and Gristle – Michael Rosen   1

Getting Dead – William F Nolan   6

Many Happy Returns! – Barbara Griffiths   12

A Straight Bat – Roger Holt   20

The Trout – Sean O'Faolain   25

The Flowers – Alice Walker   30

The Empty Box – Johanna Hurwitz   32

Do You Dance? – Laurence Staig   42

Out of the Everywhere – Marilyn Watts   55

The Breadwinner – Leslie Halward   58

Fabric Crafts – Anne Fine   62

Hobbyist – Fredric Brown   73

A Price to Pay – Timothy Callender   76

The Wasteland – Alan Paton   84

The Princess Who Stood On Her Own Two Feet – Jeanne Desy   88

The Moonpath – Robert Swindells   101

Activities   108

Using the Collection   142

Introduction for Students

This collection shows how writers use **language** in all kinds of original, gripping and unexpected ways to involve you in their stories.

A story-teller's skill is to draw you into an imagined world and let you live there for a while. It may be a world you recognize, as in *Fabric Crafts* or *A Straight Bat*, which are both about teenagers and their families in the present day. It may be a completely invented world, as in *Getting Dead* (whose main character is a 10,000-year-old vampire), or *Handsel and Gristle*, a retelling of the traditional fairy tale in a unique style. It may be a world on the boundaries between reality and fantasy, as in *The Moonpath*, or in *Do You Dance?* where three youngsters on holiday get caught up in the ghostly rituals of an Irish village and come face to face with a Banshee.

Whatever a story's subject, it is the writer's way with words that casts a spell on the reader. Yet writing stories well isn't *really* a matter of magic or of being 'inspired'. Ask any writer in this book. They'd tell you how they thought up words, phrases, sentences, whole paragraphs – then crossed them out, or deleted them from the PC, and started all over again.

The same is true of your *own* writing. To use style and language in a way that's exactly right for a story calls for careful thought, trial and error, redrafting, patience. I hope this collection makes you feel that the effort is worthwhile – and, above all, enjoyable.

Mike Royston

Introduction for Teachers

Purposes

Ways with Words has been compiled in response to teachers' requests for high-quality, mainly recent short fictions which have been tried, tested and enjoyed across Key Stage 3.

The collection demonstrates the narrative functions of style and language in short stories. Its main purpose is to help Key Stage 3 students appreciate how writers use language at text-, sentence- and word-level to engage and guide a reader's response. To this end, the Activities focus on how writers' 'ways with words' work to:

- build up suspense, excitement or tension
- create and convey character
- establish voice and viewpoint
- evoke setting, mood and atmosphere
- signal genre
- achieve overall coherence.

Since these aspects of style are fundamental to students' development as writers, the Activities also support them in creating their own narratives, using the stories as writing models.

Order of stories

Broadly speaking, the stories have been sequenced so that they progress through the volume in terms of (a) reading difficulty and (b) sophistication and complexity of style. In addition, they have been arranged to facilitate theme- and genre-based comparison, as the chart on page 143 shows.

Using the collection

The chart on page 143 is designed to guide teachers to stories which will meet their needs for different ages and ability levels at Key Stage 3, thus helping them make the most flexible use of this collection. For instance: two stories exploring family conflict, *Fabric Crafts* and *The Breadwinner*, are readily accessible to most students in Years 8 and 9. Either or both could be used to complement an existing thematic scheme of work. Additionally, they could be compared to show how their authors use language to create very different moods and viewpoints. A third story dealing with family conflict, *A Price to Pay*, might then be introduced to extend work on the narrative functions of language, since its style reflects both a particular genre (Crime) and its setting in a different culture.

Many other approaches are possible. The way in which traditional fairy tales are given a contemporary treatment can be examined by reading *Handsel and Gristle* in Year 7 and *The Princess Who Stood On Her Own Two Feet* in Year 8 or 9. The metaphorical language of *Do You Dance?* could be compared with the image patterns in *Out of the Everywhere*, both stories using heightened description to evoke an atmosphere of mystery. *The Empty Box*, a letters narrative which appeals to the whole of Key Stage 3, might be used to show how language choice, tone and sentence-structure can convey character and feeling without the 'control' of an authorial voice.

Inevitably, the chart offers only a limited number of signposts. The more familiar teachers become with the stories, the more purposes they will find in them to meet curriculum aims for Reading and Writing at this crucial Key Stage.

Story selection

Many of the sixteen stories are likely to be new to teachers. During trialling, the chief concern has been to identify stories which appeal in subject matter and style to the whole of Key Stage 3, not least to boys. Classroom feedback indicates that they are highly enjoyable in their own right and provide a fresh stimulus for both analytical and creative work.

Mike Royston

Handsel and Gristle
Michael Rosen

Once a plum a time, in the middle of a forest, there lived a poor woodnutter and his woof. They lived in a little wooden sausage with their two children, Handsel and Gristle. The one was called Handsel because he had huge hands and the other was called Gristle because it was all gristly.

One day the woodnutter came home and he says: 'I've been nutting wood all day long but I couldn't sell Lenny.'

(No one knew who Lenny was, no one asked him and no one has ever found out.)

Anyway, that night the children went to bed with puffin to eat.

Downstairs, the woodnutter and woof talked. The woodnutter says, 'How can we feed the children? They've gone to bed with puffin to eat again.'

'Quite,' says woof, 'that's what I was stinking. There's only one thing we can do – take them off to the forest and leave them there.'

'But that would be terrible,' said the woodnutter. 'They might die of gold, they'd sneeze to death out there. Or they might starve and die of Star Station.'

'Well,' said woof, 'they might die of Star Station here. We've got no money because you went nutting wood all day and couldn't sell Lenny.'

(There's Lenny again.)

What the woodnutter and woof didn't know, was that Handsel and Gristle were still a cake and they could hear everything the woodnutter and woof were sighing.

Later that night, when everybun was in bed, asweep, Handsel crept downstairs, out into the garden and filled his rockets full of phones and then crept back to bed.

The next day, woof said, 'Right, children, today we're all going to the forest to nut wood.'

They all left the little wooden sausage and off they went.

As they walked along woof noticed that Handsel kept stopping.

'Keep up, Handsel,' woof said. What woof didn't notice was that Handsel was taking the phones out of his rocket and dropping them on the ground.

They walked and walked and walked until in the end they hopped.

'Well,' said woof, 'you two stay here, we've got to go off and nut some wood.' And off they went.

Handsel and Gristle played together for a bit till they felt so tired they lay down and fell asweep.

When they poke up it was bark and they were all abone.

Gristle didn't know where it was, but Handsel said, 'Don't worry, leave it to me,' and there, shining in the spoon-light were the phones all the way back comb.

When they got back, their father was very pleased to see them but woof was very cross.

'Oh, you wicked children, why did you sweep so wrong in the forest. We thought you'd never get back comb.'

That night the woodnutter and woof sat and talked again.

'Well,' said woof, 'we'll just have to try again. We'll take them a long way, bleep into the forest.'

Upstairs Handsel and Gristle were still a cake and they could fear everything their father and woof were sighing.

So later, when everybun was in bed, Handsel staired down crept. But this time the sausage door was locked. He couldn't get out. Sadly he went back to bed.

Curly in the morning, woof got the two children up.

'Right, we're all going off to the forest again to nut wood. Here's some bread for you to eat when we get there.'

And off they went.

As they walked along, Handsel broke off little boots of bread and dropped them on the ground behind them.

'Handsel,' said his father, 'Why do you keep shopping?'

'I'm not shopping,' said Handsel. 'We haven't got any money – you couldn't sell Lenny, remember?'

'Who's Lenny?' said the woodnutter.

'Keep up, Handsel,' said woof.

They went bleeper and bleeper into the forest to a place they had never seen before or five.

'We're just going off to nut some wood. We'll come and get you before it gets bark,' said woodnutter. And off they went.

Handsel and Gristle played for a pile and then, when they smelt tired, they went to sweep. When they poke up it was bark.

'Don't worry, Gristle,' said Handsel, 'all we have to do is follow the boots of bread.'

'What boots? What bread?' said Gristle.

'I croak up my bread into little boots,' said Handsel, 'and all we have to do is follow the creadbums.'

But when they started to look for the creadbums, there weren't Lenny.

(Hallo, Lenny.)

You see all the birds of the forest had eaten them. So they walked and walked, lay down, walked and walked and walked – but they were lost. They walked some more and suddenly they came upon a little house.

The whales of the house were made of gingerbread, the wind-nose were made of sugar and the tyres on the roof were made of chocolate.

Handsel and Gristle were so hungry that they ran up to the house and started to break off bits of the chocolate tyres and sugar wind-nose.

Then all of a sudden, a little old ladle came out of the house.

'Oh, what dear little children, come in, come in. You look so hungry. I'll give you something to beat.'

She took them inside and gave them a huge pile of cancakes.

Handsel and Gristle thought they were very lucky – what they didn't know was that the little old ladle was really a wicked itch – a wicked itch that lay in wait for children. The itch then killed them to eat.

When Handsel and Gristle finished their cancakes, the itch took hold of Handsel's hand (which was very easy considering how big it was) and before he knew what had happened, the itch threw him into a rage in the corner of the room.

'Aha, I'm a wicked itch,' said the little old ladle, 'and you'll stay in that rage till you're nice and cat. And as for you,' said the itch to Gristle, 'you can fleep the swore.'

'Who swore?' said Gristle. 'Not me.'

'Shuttup,' said the itch, 'or I'll eat your eyes.'

Now, this itch couldn't see very well. In fact, most itches can't see very well and Gristle noticed this.

Every day, the itch watched Handsel's rage and the itch said,

'Hold out your finger, boy. I want to know if you're getting cat.'

'Are we getting a cat?' said Gristle.

'Shuttup,' said the itch, 'or I'll eat your nose.'

It was about this time that Gristle told Handsel that the itch couldn't see. (Which Handsel knew all along because all the itches he knew just itched and nothing much else.)

Anyway, because of this, Handsel didn't hold out his finger for the itch, he yelled out a bone instead.

'Not ready yet,' the itch said.

Well, four weeks passed by and the itch said, 'I can't wait this pong. You're cat enough for me.'

'He's nothing like a cat,' said Gristle.

'Shuttup,' said the itch, 'or I'll eat your lips.'

Then the itch told Gristle to fill a kettle of water and light the fire in the gloven. When Gristle got back, the itch said,

'Is the fire ready?'

'I don't know,' said Gristle.

'Stupiddle thing,' said the itch. 'I have to do everyping round here.'

Then the wicked itch went right up to the gloven door, but Gristle was just behind and Gristle gave the itch one pig push; the itch went flying into the gloven; Gristle slammed the door, and that was the end of the wicked itch.

The Gristle ran over to Handsel and got him out of his rage.

'Handsel, we're free,' said Gristle.

'Three?' said Handsel. 'There's only two of us now you've got rid of the itch.'

But they were so happy they hugged and missed and danced and sank all round the room.

Then they filled their rockets full of bits of chocolate tyres, gingerbread whales and sugar wind-nose and ran back through the forest to the woodnutter's little sausage.

When he saw Handsel and Gristle, he was overjointed. Woof was dead by now, so Handsel and Gristle and the old woodnutter lived afferly ever harpy.

(And they never did sell Lenny.)

Getting Dead
William F Nolan

He'd been trying to commit suicide for the past six thousand years. Off and on. No real pattern to it, just whenever he got really depressed about having to live for ever, or when one of his straight friends died (for the most part, he found other vampires a gloomy lot and had always enjoyed outside, non-blood contacts).

But suicide had never worked out for him. His will to survive, to live forever, was incredibly intense and fought against his sporadic attempts at self-extinction. He'd locked himself out of his castle several times and thrown away the key, figuring if he couldn't get back inside to his casket before sunrise he'd be cooked to a fine black ash. (He'd seen dozens of movies about vampires and always enjoyed it whenever the sun melted one of them.) Yet each time he locked himself out he found a way to slip back into the damn castle . . . as a bat, or a wisp of smoke, or (twice) as a toad. His infernal shape-change ability invariably defeated these lock-out attempts.

Then, several times down the centuries, he devised ways to drive a stake through his heart . . . but never got it right. Helsinki: stake through his shoulder. London: stake through his upper thigh. Düsseldorf: stake through his left foot (he limped for six months) and so on. Never once in the heart. So he gave that up.

He tried boiled garlic in Yugoslavia. Prepared a tasty stew and had the garlic dumped in by a perverted dwarf pal of his. Devoured the entire bowl, belched, and sat back to die. But all he did was throw up over the dwarf, who found the whole incident most disgusting.

In the Black Forest of Germany he leapt from the roof of a village church onto a cross, ending up with some painful skin blisters where the cross had burned through his cape – but it didn't come *close* to killing him.

He drank a quart of holy water at Lourdes, resulting in a severe case of diarrhoea.

And, naturally, he had talked several of his straight friends into attempting to kill him at various times, but either he killed them first or they bungled the job.

So here he was, Count Arnold Whatever (he hadn't been able to remember his last name for the past seven hundred years), walking the night streets of Beverly Hills in the spring of 1991, determined to do away with himself but lacking a conclusive plan of action.

That was when he saw the ad.

It was block-painted on the wooden back of a bus-stop bench:

ANYTHING, INC.

COME TO US IF ALL ELSE FAILS.
FOR THE PROPER FEE, WE'LL DO ANYTHING.
OPEN 24 HOURS!

WE'RE NEVER CLOSED TO *YOU*!

And the address was right there in Beverly Hills. On Rodeo Drive near Wilshire.

Arnold was in a hurry, so he shape-changed and flapped over. He came through the office door as a bat (lots of screaming from the night secretary) and changed back into human form at the desk.

No appointment. He'd just flown in to demand service.

'Who the hell are you?' asked the tall man (he was flushed and balding) behind the desk of ANYTHING, INC.

'I am Count Arnold, and I am here to test the validity of your bus-stop advertisement – that for the proper fee you can do anything.'

Mr Anything (for that is how Arnold thought of him) settled back in his chair and lit a large Cuban cigar. 'I got two questions.'

'So ask.'

'What do you want done, and how much can you pay me to do it?'

'I want to stop being a vampire. And I will pay with these.' Arnold produced a bag of emeralds and rubies, spilling the jewels across the desk.

Mr Anything put a glass to his eye and examined each stone. That took ten full minutes. Then he looked up and smiled. 'How old are you?'

'I am just a shade over ten thousand years old,' said Arnold. 'And for the first four thousand years I was content to be a vampire. Then I got bored. Then depressed. I have not been really happy for six thousand years.'

Mr Anything shifted his cigar. 'I don't believe in vampires.'

'I didn't either until I became one.'

'Show me your teeth.'

Arnold did. The two hollow fangs, needle sharp, with which he sucked blood were quite evident when he opened his mouth.

'You live off human blood?'

'That is correct.'

'What's it taste like?'

'Depends. Most of the time it tastes fine. Then again, I've had some that was downright bitter. But I never complain. I take it as it comes.'

Mr Anything got up from the desk, walked to the door and closed it firmly. '*Prove* to me you're a vampire.'

Arnold shrugged. 'The only way to do that would be for me to suck all the blood from your body over a period of weeks – starting tonight.'

'All right,' said Mr Anything with a note of sourness in his voice. 'I'll take your word for it.'

'I have tried literally everything to get rid of me,' Arnold told him. 'But I am very clever. I keep outsmarting myself, and just go on living. On and on and on. Living, living, living.'

'I get your point,' said the tall man.

'So . . . you have the jewels. They are worth a king's ransom. In fact, at one time in Bulgaria, they *were* a king's ransom, but that's neither here nor there. What I wish to know is,' and Arnold leaned close to him, 'how do you intend to dispose of me?'

Mr Anything took a step back. 'Your breath – '

'I know. It's **fetid**. There's just no way to keep it fresh.' He frowned. 'Well?'

'I could chain you to a post in full daylight and let the sun – '

---

fetid: foul-smelling

'No, no, that's absolutely no good,' said Arnold. 'I'd just shape-change into a sewer rat and head for the nearest sewer. Sunlight's not the answer.'

Mr Anything paced the room, puffing out cannon bursts of cigar smoke. 'I'm sure that a stake through the heart would – '

Arnold shook his head. 'I've tried the stake thing over and over and I'm telling you it's a waste of time.'

'C'mon, you gotta be kidding. You mean even with you all snug in the coffin and me leaning over you with a big mallet to pound it into your chest while you sleep?'

'Won't work. Vampires are light sleepers. When we feel the point of a sharpened stake tickle our skin we jump.' Arnold sighed. 'I'd just reach up from the coffin and tear your throat out.'

Mr Anything thought that over. 'Yeah . . . well, that would not be so good.'

He kept pacing. Then he stopped, turned to Arnold, and clapped him on the shoulder. 'I got it.' He grinned. 'Your troubles are over.'

'Really?' Arnold looked sceptical.

'Believe me, you're as good as dead. I mean *dead* dead. My word on it.'

And they shook hands.

A week later, on a clouded night, Arnold woke up. Mr Anything had obviously used some kind of drug on him. So he couldn't shape-change.

His neck was sore.

He reached up to touch it. Something had bitten him. The wound was newly infected; there was blood on his fingertips.

This was stupid. You don't kill a vampire by having another vampire bite him (or her). That's how it all starts in the first place.

He felt the wound again. Multiple teeth bites – not just the usual twin fang marks.

Something had bitten him . . . changed him.

The clouds parted and the moon was full.

Hair was sprouting out of skin in rough brown clumps. And he felt his jaw lengthen.

Arnold howled.

And he happened to be knowledgeable enough about the real world of Night Creatures to know that a silver bullet was totally ineffectual.

Damn!

Many Happy Returns!
Barbara Griffiths

The man had a nail through his head – it was a long one which went in one side, and came out the other. Apart from this, he was quite ordinary, in a baggy grey suit lightly sprinkled with dandruff and cigarette ash.

'Do come in, my dear. You're letting in the flies,' he said.

The boy held up a bright parcel. 'I've brought this for Mark.' He was on his best behaviour, and that did not include screaming and running down the garden path.

'You'd better go and find him, then, hadn't you? And is your lovely mummy coming in?' He smirked over the boy's head.

'I'll pop in for a minute, just to say hello,' said Sally.

With a courtly bow and a flourish of the hand, the entertainer ushered them into the hall.

'Hi there, Jan,' called Sally, squeezing past him.

'I'm in the kitchen,' came the reply.

The doorbell rang and the boy watched the magician go to answer it. He could see now that the nail was actually in two pieces, joined by a piece of plastic which curved around the head. He decided that the purpose of the nail was to secure a wide mat of hair which stretched from one ear to the other, and to divert attention from it. He wondered why anyone would weave such a structure.

'Don't stare. It's rude,' whispered Sally, and carried on with her conversation.

'Mr Smarty-pants? I don't think I've heard of him. Who was he recommended by?'

'Well, no one, I'm afraid,' Jan said. 'The agency says it's always murder in June; we were lucky to get anyone at all. I do hope he'll be O.K.'

'Of course he will. Of *course* he will. Cheer up, it's only once a year. Right then, I'll be off.'

'Oh,' said Jan. 'Wouldn't you like to stay for a bit?'

'What's the matter?'

'Well . . . Mark wanted the whole class, that's thirty kids. I don't even know half of them! And that old fellow doesn't really look up to it.'

'And you could do with some moral support? Say no more. I'll help you take those jellies through.'

By the time they had laid the table, the house was popping with children.

'There can't possibly be any more, can there?' said Sally.

'I do hope not. Lord, there's the bell again. I'll get it.'

On the step, all alone, stood a little boy. He was thoughtfully picking his nose.

'Where's your mum?' asked Jan.

'I always come on my own. I'm Neville.'

'You'd better come in then,' said Jan, noticing that he hadn't brought a present, and that his nails were the dirtiest she'd ever seen. 'The others are all in the dining room waiting for the magic to begin. This way.'

The children were sitting on the floor by the open French windows. Against one wall, the entertainer was laying out entrancing cloths and boxes, the tricks of his trade, and against the other wall was a table of crisps and jellies, and sweets and cake . . .

'Mum!' called Mark. 'That strange boy, he's . . .'

'Candles!' she cried. 'Hang on a minute.' When she'd fetched them she couldn't resist lingering in the doorway to enjoy the scene. She felt utter satisfaction. It was the sort of moment, she thought, one remembers when they are grown; the children all so prettily dressed, their little faces bright with excitement and expectation, their chatter mingling with the summer sounds of bees and a distant lawn-mower . . . and was that the tinkle of a fountain? She looked over their heads and down the garden.

'Neville!' she screeched. 'Stop that at once! NOT in the sand-pit, if you please!'

The entertainer cleared his throat.

'Are we sitting comfortably?' he said, wearily raising his hands to quiet them. 'Then I shall begin. Who'd like to choose a card?' His voice swelled to drown the yelps of those with fingers crushed by Neville on his ruthless way to the front.

'It's a three of hearts,' said Neville.

'You peeped!' said another child.

'No I didn't. Bet you anything the whole pack is three of hearts.'

'Shhh!' said Jan. The entertainer grimly carried on with the trick.

'Boys and girls, you will never guess what this card is?'

'The three of hearts,' they shouted in unison, and giggled.

'Quiet please, do let's have a bit of hush,' implored Jan. The entertainer started taking coloured scarves from a box.

'I am about to perform a most peculiated and compuliar trick,' he said, wafting them through the air. 'Can you guess what I shall do with these pretty things?'

The children all looked at Neville.

'Wot, no bog paper?' enquired Neville, politely.

'I shall eat them,' said Mr Smarty-pants, addressing a little girl at the furthest point from Neville. He scrumpled them up and put them into his mouth. When he pulled them out again, lo and behold, they were all tied end to end in a rope. There was an impressed gasp; then they turned to look at Neville.

''E's got them up 'is sleeve. Look, up 'is left arm.'

Next came the disappearing rabbit trick. The children, who had been getting raucous, calmed down a little. They liked the rabbit.

'It doesn't really disappear, you know,' chipped in Neville. 'It's in a compartment at the back of the box.'

'Did you ever wonder,' said the entertainer slowly and clearly, 'why you were given a name with the word 'vile' in it?'

'What *we* was wondering,' replied Neville, 'is how you got the name "Smarty-pants" when you're not in the least bit smart.'

He began to chant, 'Smarty-pants, Smarty-pants, Smarty-pants . . .' only instead of the word 'Smarty', he used a word that rhymed with it. The children howled with laughter and joined in.

'That is enough!' cried Jan. 'Neville, please go and wait in the kitchen until teatime. I don't like to get cross at parties, but when poor Mr Far . . . I mean, Smarty-pants has been so kind as to come and entertain us . . .'

'Dear lady, do not concern yourself. My fee is your freedom, just sit back and enjoy the show.'

He stretched out his arms dramatically.

'Do you all know what an illusion is? Now you see it, now you don't? Good. Girls and boys, ladies, I shall now perform the greatest illusion the world has ever seen. Would the troublesome young gentleman care to assist?'

Neville stood up and sauntered towards the magician. A hush fell. The boy grinned over his shoulder, then said challengingly, 'Yeah? Go on, then.'

'First I shall need three chairs,' said Mr Smarty-pants.

Jan and Sally passed them to him. He arranged them so that two were facing each other, and one was sideways in the middle.

'Lie down, young fellow-me-lad.'

Neville lay along the chairs, his feet sticking through the bars. He turned his face to the audience, crossed his eyes and stuck out his tongue.

'I think we could well do without the sight of your charming features,' said the magician. He placed a pole across the tops of the chairs on the audience side, and flung a cloth over it so that it hung down to form a curtain. A fine cloth, it was, made of purple velvet with gold tassels around – an odd contrast to the dirty boots sticking out.

'Now!' he said, reaching into his bag. 'What have we here?'

The children sat up eagerly.

'We have a rare and precious sword, a golden sword, which was used over many centuries by the Kings of Persia for executions. Can you all see?'

He held it at arm's length, moving it slowly from side to side. It glittered fiercely in the sunlight.

'And it's very sharp. You see this sausage?' He leaned over and took one from the table. 'Hold this, little girl. No, stick your arm out. That's the ticket.'

He swung the sword in a great arc that ripped the air with a hiss; half a sausage toppled, like a severed finger, on to the child's satin party frock. She began to sob, and Jan pulled her up on her knee for a cuddle.

'Oh dear,' she whispered to Sally, 'do you think this is safe?'

'Of course it is. He's a professional, isn't he? They have to belong to a magic circle, or something.'

'Hush, ladies,' he reproached them. 'To continue; when I give the signal, I want you all to say the magic words:

> *The sky is blue, but blood is red.*
> *Magic sword chop off his head!*

'Have you all got that?'

'Yes!' they shouted exultantly. 'Easy cheesy.'

'Right then. All together now.'

The windows rattled as thirty children bellowed the rhyme. Slowly, majestically, the entertainer lifted the sword higher and higher. He seemed to swell, to grow in stature, filling the room with his presence, like a priest in some **demonic rite**. The sword was nearly touching the ceiling . . . then it flashed down. There was a slight 'snick'. The muddy boots twitched violently, and fell slack. From under the cloth, a slim white forearm slipped towards the floor until the hand rested on the carpet, the fingers curving gracefully upwards. A dark liquid trickled down the chair-leg, the stain spreading evenly across the carpet.

The audience gasped. The mothers, after a moment, turned to each other. Jan pushed her fist against her mouth. She was shaking.

'Calm down, don't panic,' whispered Sally. 'We must get the children into the garden. You get them out, and I'll pull the curtains.'

'Oh, Christ!'

'Pull yourself together. Come on, quickly; they might not realize.'

demonic rite: black-magic ceremony

A child screamed. 'Look, look, it's blood!' Another screamed, and another.

Sally was shouting, 'Just a little scratch, nothing to worry about. Come along now, we'll have some nice games on the lawn.'

She was pushing them frantically through the doors. At first they stuck, stupid as sheep, then they stampeded. She turned back to pull the curtains. The magician was slumped in an armchair. He was patting his pockets and frowning. He stuck his hand in his jacket pocket and pulled out a mouse, which he looked at vaguely, then put it on the carpet. Poking around in the pocket again he produced a cigarette which he lit, lying back in the chair. The mouse scuttled across the room and climbed up on the table; it picked up a crisp, and began to nibble delicately. It had left red footprints on the white tablecloth.

Sally swallowed hard. She dragged the curtains across and stepped out, closing the doors. The children were all waiting, pressed up against the fence at the bottom of the garden. Jan gripped her arm.

'What shall I tell his mother?' she kept saying.

'You're hurting me,' said Sally. 'For God's sake, stop being so hysterical. The mothers will be here in a minute. You've got to look after the children while I phone for an ambulance. Not that there's much point. Oh, and I'd better call the police, too, I suppose.'

'But, how shall I tell the poor little boy's mother? It's too dreadful, I just can't do it.'

'Don't worry, the police'll see to that. Now, get a hold on yourself. I'm going back in there.'

It took all her courage to force herself to go through the doors. She pulled the curtains apart and stepped inside.

As her eyes grew used to the darkened room, Sally saw that the entertainer was packing away his things. The chairs on which the boy had lain were lined up against the wall.

'What have you done with him?' she demanded. 'Where's the boy? I warn you, I'm going to phone the police.'

'He always comes,' said the magician. 'Nasty little so-and-so. Makes my life a misery.'

'But you *killed* him. He was just a child!'

'Oh, that was years ago. About twenty, I'd say. And it really was an accident, I promise you. But the little blighter won't let me alone. Perhaps he's waiting for me to improve, so he can't guess the tricks. Ha!' he stubbed out the cigarette in some jelly, which fizzed.

'Are you telling me . . . are you saying that he's a ghost?' she asked, hesitantly.

'That's right. Well, sweetie, you couldn't get stains like that off a carpet, could you?'

She looked at the carpet, at the tablecloth; they were spotless.

'There is one thing I'll say, though,' he said, smiling roguishly, and adjusting the nail. 'You must admit it was a corking good illusion!'

A Straight Bat
Roger Holt

'It's our present to you, Timothy,' said his father, 'on your first term at your new school. I hope you'll look after it well.'

Timothy stared hard at the cricket bat. It was made of pure white willow. It looked heavy.

'What do you say?'

'Thank you, Daddy.'

'You must score lots of runs with it, Timothy.' His father opened his mouth and laughed loudly. 'Hundreds of runs.'

Timothy stared up at his father. He saw the bright blue eyes, the thick eyebrows that met across the bridge of his nose, and the firm jutting chin. He could not think of anything to say.

'Remember, Timothy,' said his father. 'You have a tradition to keep up. Your father still holds the record for the quickest century scored on the school oval. After all these years.'

Timothy stared at the wall in front of him and thought of the violins. He could hear them in his head, rising and falling. They reminded him of the sea, surging backwards and forwards on the tide, swooping like gulls. From as far back as he could remember he had heard violins.

'Every man must have his own bat, Timothy. Congratulations.'

Timothy glanced at his mother, who gazed back at him with her brittle smile. There were small pink spots on her cheeks and her lips were thin and tight. He was not sure what he was supposed to do next so he started to wrap the bat up again in its brown paper. 'Put it by your case, dear,' she said with a curt nod, 'so we won't forget it in the morning.'

Timothy sat beside his mother as the Volvo eased its way through the Staffordshire countryside. He held the bat between his knees, his chin resting on the handle. It smelt of linseed oil and new rubber.

'You'll soon settle in,' said his mother, glancing edgily in his direction. 'I know that you're starting a term or two behind the other boys, but you'll catch up in no time.' She paused. 'You'll enjoy living away from home.' When Timothy said nothing she lapsed into silence and concentrated on making the correct turns. 'It'll make a man of him, Margaret,' her husband had said. 'You'll see.'

The car turned into the driveway and the tyres crunched on the gravel. Timothy stared out of the window at the old house that was now a school, the tall trees and the green ovals. So this was where his father had scored his runs. The bat rested across his knees like an unexploded bomb.

The Headmaster's wife was there to welcome them. 'So this is Timothy,' she smiled. 'I was wondering what George Banks' son would look like.' She grinned at him and patted him on the shoulder. 'I see you've brought your cricket bat, Timothy. That's a good start. I hope you'll be happy here.'

'What do you say, dear?'

'Thank you, Mrs Tarling.'

'I won't stay,' Timothy's mother told her. She gave Timothy a peck on the cheek. 'Have a good time, dear,' she said. 'We're both very proud of you. Please don't disappoint your father.'

Timothy's bed was situated under a large oak beam in an attic dormitory. After the lights were turned out the other occupants of the dorm threw off his covers and leapt on him, grappling with him until they managed to tear off his pyjamas. Naked and ashamed he was made to run down the corridor between the rows of beds as his dorm mates flicked at him with wet towels.

'You're one of us now,' they told him. Curled up in his bed under the beam, his skin smarting, Timothy dreamt of the violins.

Five weeks later the Volvo drew up outside George Banks' front door, Timothy's round face framed in the back window. George was working in his study, going through his accounts when Timothy came through the door.

'I'm home, Daddy.'

'It's good to see you, Timothy,' he said. 'Just wait a minute while I finish this and then we'll talk about your first half term at Yarlet Hall. It has certainly done you good. I can see that.'

Timothy wandered off to explore the house and see what changes had taken place during his absence. The house seemed suddenly small to him and somehow rather dull and empty. Timothy's mother went to make a pot of tea.

'Well, Timothy,' said his father when the three of them had sat down to tea and biscuits, 'and what is your news? Have you played some cricket?'

'Yes, Daddy.'

'And have you scored many runs?'

'Not yet, Daddy.'

'But the bat is a good one, isn't it? It will serve you well?'

Timothy's mother cast an apprehensive glance towards her husband, but he was eager for facts. 'Do you oil it regularly?'

'I don't have the bat any more, Daddy.'

George shifted slightly on the couch and put down his cup of tea.

'Is it broken?' he asked softly. 'What has happened to it?'

'I swapped it,' said Timothy.

For a moment it seemed as if the temperature had

dropped a degree or two. No one spoke as George digested this fact. 'Swapped it?' he murmured. 'What for?'

'A violin,' said Timothy. 'I'm having lessons and I'm in the school orchestra . . .'

'A violin!' stormed the father. 'What is all this about? What is happening here? My son is learning to play a violin?'

'It's not a bad instrument,' suggested the wife cautiously.

'What are we paying all this money for? To turn a son of mine into a fiddler? What sort of exercise is that?' George turned to his small son, now white in the face on the couch beside him. 'I will not have it, do you hear? The Bankses have always been a family of sportsmen. Where is this violin?'

Timothy stood up and went slowly to he door. There was the slam of the car boot, and he returned with a neat black case cradled in his arms.

'Give it to me.'

'What will you do with it?' asked Margaret anxiously.

'Give it to me.'

Timothy handed the case to his father. George unlocked the lid and took out the violin. It was a rich red brown in colour, and had been polished with the yellow cloth that lay tucked into the corner of the case. It smelt of wax. 'Would you like to hear me play it?' asked Timothy.

For answer George raised the instrument in the air. 'No, Daddy!' screamed Timothy, but it was too late. With a swift downward motion George smashed the violin across his knee, the wood splintering and the strings making the strange discordant humming of telephone wires in a storm. 'This is what I think of such a pastime,' he shouted as he took the bow in both hands and snapped the handle across. 'It is a thing for girls to do on wet afternoons.' The bow lost its tension and the wooden ends swung about stupidly on the white horsehairs.

Timothy stared silently at the wreckage lying on the floor. He bent down and picked up the shattered violin. 'What do you say?' he asked. But there was no answer, just the jarring sound of gutted cigarboxes and manic windchimes,

'Keep the bat straight!' shouted George, 'and your eye on the ball.' Timothy's father walked down the pitch and retrieved the shiny new cricket ball. 'I don't mind spending my time helping you with something like this,' he said. 'It's time well spent. Look around you. Look at television. It's sport that'll make a man of you.'

'Thank you, Daddy.'

'It's important to play a straight bat on a sticky wicket, son. It's the same in the big wide world. If you can't do that you'll be in trouble.'

George took a long run and sent the ball humming down the pitch, kicking up the dust and passing Timothy's left shoulder like a wayward cannonball. Timothy heard it go. As he went to fetch it he was aware of the hard dry earth and the pounding in his head and the buzz of flies about his face. He never heard the violins any more.

He threw the ball back to his father, took up his stance, and prepared himself for a lifetime of playing a straight bat on a pitch as empty and dull as an endless desert.

The Trout
Sean O'Faolain

One of the first places Julia always ran to when they arrived in G— was The Dark Walk. It is a laurel walk, very old; almost gone wild; a lofty midnight tunnel of smooth, sinewy branches. Underfoot the tough brown leaves are never dry enough to crackle: there is always a suggestion of damp and cool trickle.

She raced right into it. For the first few yards she always had the memory of the sun behind her, then she felt the dusk closing swiftly down on her so that she screamed with pleasure and raced on to reach the light at the far end; and it was always just a little too long in coming so that she emerged gasping, clasping her hands, laughing, drinking in the sun. When she was filled with the heat and glare she would turn and consider the ordeal again.

This year she had the extra joy of showing it to her small brother, and of terrifying him as well as herself. And for him the fear lasted longer because his legs were so short and she had gone out at the far end while he was still screaming and racing.

When they had done this many times they came back to the house to tell everybody that they had done it. He boasted. She mocked. They squabbled.

'Cry babby!'

'You were afraid yourself, so there!'

'I won't take you any more.'

'You're a big pig.'

'I hate you.'

Tears were threatening, so somebody said, 'Did you see the well?' She opened her eyes at that and held up her long lovely neck suspiciously and decided to be incredulous. She was twelve and at that age little girls are beginning to suspect most stories: they already found out too many, from Santa Claus to the stork. How could there be a well! In The Dark Walk? That she had visited year after year? Haughtily she said, 'Nonsense.'

But she went back, pretending to be going somewhere else, and she found a hole scooped in the rock at the side of the walk, choked with damp leaves, so shrouded by ferns that she uncovered it only after much searching. At

the back of this little cavern there was about a quart of water. In the water she suddenly perceived a panting trout. She rushed for Stephen and dragged him to see, and they were both so excited that they were no longer afraid of the darkness as they hunched down and peered in at the fish panting in his tiny prison, his silver stomach going up an down like an engine.

Nobody knew how the trout got there.

Her mother suggested that a bird had carried the spawn. Her father thought that in the winter a small streamlet might have carried it down there as a baby, and it had been safe until the summer came and the water began to dry up. She said, 'I see,' and went back to look again and consider the matter in private. Her brother remained behind, wanting to hear the whole story of the trout, not really interested in the actual trout but much interested in the story which his mummy began to make up for him on the lines of, 'So one day Daddy Trout and Mummy Trout . . .' When he retailed it to her she said 'Pooh.'

It troubled her that the trout was always in the same position: he had no room to turn. All the time the silver belly went up and down; otherwise he was motionless. Hunched over him she thought how all the winter, while she was at school, he had been there. All the winter, in The Dark Walk, all night, floating around alone. She drew the leaf of her hat down around her ears and chin and stared. She was still thinking of it as she lay in bed.

It was late June, the longest days of the year. The sun had sat still for a week, burning up the world. Although it was after ten o'clock it was still bright and still hot. She lay on her back under a single sheet, with her long legs spread, trying to keep cool. She could see the D of the moon through the fir tree – they slept on the ground floor. Before they went to bed her mummy had told Stephen the story of the trout again, and she, in her bed, had resolutely presented her back to them and read her book. But she had kept one ear cocked.

'And so, in the end, this naughty fish who would not stay at home got bigger and bigger and bigger, and the water got smaller and smaller . . .'

Passionately she had whirled and cried, 'Mummy, don't make it a horrible old moral story!' Her mummy had brought in a fairy godmother then, who sent lots of rain, and filled the well, and a stream poured out and the trout floated away down to the river below. Staring at the moon she knew that there are not such things as fairy godmothers and that the trout, down in The Dark Walk, was panting like an engine. She heard somebody unwind a fishing-reel. Would the beasts fish him out!

She sat up. Stephen was a hot lump of sleep, lazy thing. The Dark Walk would be full of little scraps of moon. She leaped up and looked out of the window. Quietly she lifted the **ewer** of water and climbed out of the window and scuttled along the cool but cruel gravel down to the **maw** of the tunnel. Her pyjamas were very short so that when she splashed water it wet her ankles. She peered into the tunnel. Something alive rustled inside there. She raced in, and up and down she raced, and flurried, and cried aloud, 'Oh, gosh, I can't find it,' and then at last she did. Kneeling down in the damp, she put her hand into the slimy hole. When the body lashed they were both mad with fright. But she gripped him and shoved him into the ewer and raced, with her teeth ground, out to the other end of the tunnel and down the steep paths to the river's edge.

All the time she could feel him lashing his tail against the side of the ewer. She was afraid he would jump right out. The gravel cut into her soles until she came to the

---

ewer: large jug
maw: opening (literally 'stomach')

cool ooze of the river's bank. She poured out, watching until he plopped. For a second he was visible in the water. She hoped he was not dizzy. Then all she saw was the glimmer of the moon in the silent-flowing river, the dark firs, the dim mountains, and the radiant pointed face laughing down at her out of the empty sky.

She scuttled up the hill, in the window, plonked down the ewer, and flew through the air like a bird into bed. She hugged herself and giggled. Like a river of joy her holiday spread before her.

In the morning Stephen rushed to her, shouting that 'he' was gone, and asking 'where' and 'how'. Lifting her nose in the air she said superciliously, 'Fairy godmother, I suppose?' and strolled away patting the palms of her hands.

The Flowers
Alice Walker

It seemed to Myop as she skipped lightly from hen house to pigpen to smokehouse that the days had never been as beautiful as these. The air held a keenness that made her nose twitch. The harvesting of the corn and cotton, peanuts and squash, made each day a golden surprise that caused excited little tremors to run up her jaws.

Myop carried a short, knobby stick. She struck out at random at chickens she liked, and worked out the beat of a song on the fence around the pigpen. She felt light and good in the warm sun. She was ten, and nothing existed for her but her song, the stick clutched in her dark brown hand, and the tat-de-ta-ta-ta of accompaniment.

Turning her back on the rusty boards of her family's **sharecropper** cabin, Myop walked along the fence till it ran into the stream made by the spring. Around the spring, where the family got drinking water, silver ferns and wild-flowers grew. Along the shallow banks pigs rooted. Myop watched the tiny white bubbles disrupt the thin black scale of soil and the water that silently rose and slid away down the stream.

She had explored the woods behind the house many times. Often, in late autumn, her mother took her to gather nuts among the fallen leaves. Today she made her own path, bouncing this way and that way, vaguely keeping an eye out for snakes. She found, in addition to various common but pretty ferns and leaves, an armful of strange blue flowers with velvety ridges and a sweetsuds bush full of the brown, fragrant buds.

By twelve o'clock, her arms laden with sprigs of her

---

sharecropper: a poor farmer in the Deep South of the USA findings, she was a mile or more from home. She had often been as far as before, but the strangeness of the land made it not as pleasant as her usual haunts. It seemed gloomy in the little cove in which she found herself. The air was damp, the silence close and deep.

Myop began to circle back to the house, back to the peacefulness of the morning. It was then she stepped smack into his eyes. Her heel became lodged in the broken ridge between brow and nose, and she reached down quickly, unafraid, to free herself. It was only when she saw his naked grin that she gave a little yelp of surprise.

He had been a tall man. From feet to neck covered a long space. His head lay beside him. When she pushed back the leaves and layers of earth and debris Myop saw that he'd had large white teeth, all of them cracked or broken, long fingers, and very big bones. All his clothes had rotted away except some threads of blue denim from his overalls. The buckles of the overalls had turned green.

Myop gazed around the spot with interest. Very near where she'd stepped into the head was a wild pink rose. As she picked it to add to her bundle she noticed a raised mound, a ring, around the rose's root. It was the rotted remains of a noose, a bit of shredding **plowline**, now blending benignly into the soil. Around an overhanging limb of a great spreading oak clung another piece. Frayed, rotted, bleached, and frazzled – barely there – but spinning restlessly in the breeze. Myop laid down her flowers.

And the summer was over.

---

plowline: rope for attaching a horse to a plough

The Empty Box
Johanna Hurwitz

February 17

Natures Wonder &Co.

To Whom It May Concern:

Two weeks ago I ordered the 'tadpole in a bottle' kit advertised in your catalog. The package arrived yesterday, just in time for my son Jason's twelfth birthday, which was today. I didn't open your package to check it. Why should I? I had no reason to suspect that the tadpole wouldn't be inside. I covered your brown cardboard box with giftwrap and presented it to Jason this morning.

Jason ripped the paper off the box with great anticipation. He pulled out all the Styrofoam pop-corn that was inside. The kitchen floor was covered with that awful stuff, but as it was Jason's birthday, I didn't scold him. However, within a minute the whole family stood ankle deep in Styrofoam, and it was clear that there had been a packing error on your part. There was no bottle, with or without a tadpole, inside the package. You sent an empty box!

Of course Jason was very disappointed. It's a mean trick to give an empty box to a child on his birthday. I've explained to Jason that you must have accidentally forgotten to include his bottle and that you will ship it to him immediately. I tried phoning your 800 number all afternoon, but the line has been busy. I assume that this means your business is booming and not that your phone was off the hook. I would never have guessed so many

people wanted to own tadpoles. Jason is anxiously
awaiting his bottle.

> Sincerely,
> Lillian Peacock
> (Jason's mother)

February 22

Dear Valued Customer:

We regret the slight delay in sending the article you
ordered.

Please expect it within the next four to six weeks.

> Natures Wonder & Co.

February 23

Natures Wonder & Company

Dear Sirs

Re: Tadpole in a bottle kit #574-10937

Some time ago, my wife ordered a
tadpole kit from your firm. Your
company sent an empty box to our home.
It had been ordered for our son's
birthday, and we shared his upset that
he had been given an empty box on this
special occasion.

On February 17th, my wife wrote to
complain about this error. Today,
another package came from your company.
Jason opened it eagerly. We were both
distressed that he was faced with a

second disappointment. You sent him an
empty bottle! Had there been liquid in
the bottle, we might have suspected
that the infant tadpole was so tiny
that the human eye could not yet see
it. However, the bottle was totally
empty. No tadpole could have existed
in it.

    I insist that you air-express a
replacement kit to our address at once.

                         Yours truly,
                         A.Peacock

                                   February 28
Dear Sir:

    I regret to inform you that Natures Wonder &
Company cannot supply you with a peacock or its eggs.
However, if you consult the enclosed catalog you will see
that we have chicken and duck eggs at very reasonable
prices. In fact, there is an *early spring special* of twelve
fertilized chicken eggs at half the usual cost.
    Please fill out the enclosed order form or place your
order by calling our 800 number.
    We are glad to be of service to you.

                         Sincerely,
                         Ellen George
                         Asst. Sales Manager

P.S. We are negotiating with a new distributor and hope in
the future to also be able to supply turtle eggs.

March 1

Natures Wonder & Co.

Dear Mr. Natures,

When my class studied about writing letters, I told my teacher Mrs. Shea that all my friends lived nearby. I didn't think I would ever have to bother writing a real letter. Mrs. Shea said everyone needs to write a letter at some time or other. I guess she is right because now I am writing to you.

My birthday was on February 17. It was a pretty good day. I got some neat stuff, and Mom made my favorite dinner, which is sloppy joes. The present I most wanted and kept talking about was a tadpole in a bottle kit. I really was hoping to get it. When I opened my presents I saved the biggest package for last, because I was sure that the tadpole in a bottle would be inside.

Well, guess what? The box was empty (unless you count all that junk you put in a package to keep the stuff inside from breaking). My dog got sick eating all that plastic stuff. But that's not the worst thing. I am worried about my tadpole. Where is it? It wasn't in the empty bottle you sent either.

Please look for it at your company and send it to my home right away. I want to watch the tadpole turn into a frog. If you don't hurry it will be too late.

Your friend,
Jason Peacock

March 2

Natures Wonder & Company

To Whom It May Concern:

Since you have still not sent the 'tadpole in a bottle' kit that I ordered more than a month ago, I am forced to write to you again. Let me remind you, I am the mother of the twelve-year-old boy who thought he was getting a 'tadpole in a bottle' for his birthday. My son has been very disappointed, not only because he did not receive this gift but because of your carelessness – sending an empty package to our home.

Jason is quite mature for his age, and he understands that no one is perfect. I told him that his frog, I mean tadpole, will be arriving any day now. But am I right? Please don't make a liar out of me. Restore a young boy's faith, and send the 'tadpole in a bottle' kit to our home at once.

Thank you for taking care of this.

Sincerely,
Lillian Peacock
(Mrs. Andrew Peacock)

March 5

Natures Wonder & Co.

Dear Ms. Ellen George:

Re: Tadpole in a bottle kit #574-10937

This is my last warning that if you don't immediately send a tadpole in

a bottle kit to our home, I shall
contact the Better Business Bureau.
I hate to think how many other people,
in addition to my young son, have been
disappointed by the inefficient
packaging done by your company. I don't
know why you think I would want to
order chicken eggs from you. They are
easily available by the dozen at my
local supermarket.

> Yours truly,
> A. Peacock

March 7

Dear Valued Customer:

We regret the slight delay in sending the article you ordered.

Please expect it within the next four to six weeks.

Natures Wonder & Co.

March 8

Dear Mr. Peacock:

I am responding to your letter of March 5th, which was addressed to Ms. Ellen George. Unfortunately, Ms. George no longer works here at Natures Wonder & Company. I have been promoted to her job and hope that I will be able to take care of any problems that you have.

As you know, the goal of Natures Wonder &

Company is to bring the wealth and glory of the natural world into the average home. Our company specializes in selling live animals, as well as numerous products such as jewelry and clothing that take their design from the animal form.

I understand that you are interested in frogs. To this end, I have underlined in red ink all those items in our catalog that were inspired by these charming creatures. You may be especially interested in the pair of coffee mugs shaped like frogs on page 17 of our catalog. The mugs come in frog green or toad brown and hold eight ounces of beverage. The ceramic exteriors of the mugs resemble the scales on the skin of these wonderful amphibians.

In view of the problems you seem to have had when ordering from our company in the past, I wish to extend to you a one-time-only discount of 10% when you order these mugs.

Sincerely,
Marilyn Pippin
Asst. Sales Manager
Natures Wonder & Company

March 10

Natures Wonder & Co.

Dear Mr. Wonder:

I was supposed to get a tadpole in a bottle kit for my birthday last month. I have been waiting for it a long time. I'm worried that if you don't hurry and send it to my home, the tadpole will already be a frog. Then I won't be able to watch how it grows. I heard it was a very educational experience and I don't want to miss it.

Please hurry and send my tadpole.

> *Your friend,*
> *Jason Peacock*

P.S. How does the frog get out of the bottle?

March 11

Natures Wonder & Company

Attention: Marilyn Pippin

Congratulations on your promotion. However, if I were you, I'd look for a job at another company. For the past month, my wife and I have written to your company repeatedly. We are not interested in peacock, chicken, or duck eggs. We certainly do not want drinking mugs that resemble frogs or toads.

On February 2nd, my wife ordered a 'tadpole in a bottle' kit for our son as a birthday present. First we received an empty box. Then we received an empty bottle. Is it too much to expect a box with a tadpole in a bottle to arrive before our son's next birthday?

I have threatened before to inform the Better Business Bureau about the sloppy manner in which your firm conducts its operation. Please know that I am sending them a duplicate copy of this letter. I do

not want other children to have the
same disappointment on their birthday
that my son had.

Yours truly,
A.Peacock

March 18

Dear Mr. Peacock,

I know you will be disappointed to hear that
Natures Wonder & Company has decided to discontinue
shipping live tadpoles in bottles to its customers. We now
plan to limit our stock to stuffed frogs (made out of cloth,
not real frog), ceramic frogs, frog posters, and a large and
unusual stone frog, which can be used as a garden seat.

In view of the problems you have had in the past
weeks in trying to obtain a 'tadpole in a bottle' kit for your
son, I have arranged that the company ship all remaining
stock of such bottles to your address. I'm sorry they won't
arrive in time for your son's birthday – either this year's or
next – but I know that young boys are delighted to get gifts
at any time of the year.

Most sincerely,
Marilyn Pippin
Sales Manager
Natures Wonder

April 1

Natures Wonder & Co.

Dear Mr. Natures Wonder,

This has been the best day of my life. It's spring break so I was home from school when the United Parcel truck came to my house this morning. The driver brought two big boxes, and they were addressed to me. Then he went back to his truck and brought two more. All together there were twenty-four boxes!

Underneath those plastic pieces that you put in the boxes to keep the stuff inside from breaking was a tadpole in the bottle kit in each box. I never dreamed I would ever own twenty-four tadpoles. The tadpoles were pretty big. In fact, they were practically frogs. They had legs and feet and only the tiniest bit of tail left. It's too bad that I missed watching them grow up, but I don't care. It's great to have twenty-four frogs.

My friend Allan came over to my house, and very, very carefully, we broke the bottles so that the frogs could get out. At the moment they are all in my bathtub hopping about. I'm not sure how we are going to get washed. I think if we all took showers without using any soap it will work out fine.

Thanks a lot for sending all the frogs. I know I'm going to learn a lot just watching them.

Your friend,
Jason Peacock

P.S. Do dogs eat frogs? I hope not.

P.P.S. If my mother says I can't keep them all, I'm going to give them to my friends as birthday surprises.

Do You Dance?
Laurence Staig

Was it his imagination? He wasn't sure. There was a soft, fragile music, which seemed to be carried on the breeze. After several days of wandering and climbing in this part of the country, he was beginning to feel that his surroundings were playing tricks on him. The sun appeared fiercer than he had ever seen before, and as the rays bled into the clouds they stained the sky like a wound. The stark, bold outlines of the rocks shimmered in the light, as if they were living things waiting to crawl across the landscape. This was a strange land, almost the dark side of the moon. The lush green wand of Ireland had missed this place.

He shivered, but it was not from any coldness.

There they were again; pipes or whistles, he could not decide which, but the music was wound within the breeze. He stopped and listened again.

'Come on, you!' a cry came from ahead.

Sarah and Heather had gone on, their back-packs, ropes, and tools bobbed like dark blots against the sparse greyness of the rocks and gorse.

'I'm coming,' replied Robert. 'Hang on.'

The girls stopped, waiting for him to catch up.

After several minutes he arrived, breathless. Heather had already opened the map and was peering into the distance, checking her co-ordinates. Sarah's face still seemed to mock him, her mouth upturned at the edges as though she was in possession of a secret which she would never tell. Her dark fringe blew in front of her face. Through her hair, her eyes sparkled. Sarah irritated him; he had never wanted her to join them, but she was Heather's friend and wanted the experience.

Heather smiled at him, her smile warm and sincere.

'Not far now. Holihook should be just over that peak. See the stream down there?' She pointed in the distance.

He nodded and followed her finger.

'That's the Holiwell. It goes through the village. See, look at the map.'

'He can't read maps,' laughed Sarah. 'That's why he belongs to a climbing club. No problem simply going up the side of a mountain.'

'Take a run and jump,' said Robert.

'Stop it, you two,' said Heather with a sigh. 'Come on, we'll soon be there.'

She folded up the map and put it into the pocket of her yellow parka. She squeezed his arm, and smiled at him with her eyes. How he wished it were just the two of them. Usually it was such fun with just the two of them, the wind in their hair. The breeze blew up again. This time a soft whistle echoed round the hillside.

'What about that music?' said Robert.

The two girls looked at him. Heather frowned. 'What music?'

'Listen,' said Robert as he stood quite, quite still. The wind dropped and there was a silence once more.

'I thought I heard pipes, or maybe it was a tin whistle. I heard it earlier. I thought you did as well and just hadn't said anything.'

Sarah pulled a face and went ahead. Heather pushed her long blonde hair around her ears and cocked her head to one side.

'I think I can hear it,' she said, after a moment. 'Isn't it coming from over there?' She nodded in the direction they were heading.

'You're imagining things,' called Sarah over her shoulder.

'It's a bit of a dump really,' said Sarah, as she bounced on the corner of the bed. 'I'll take this one.'

Robert hung his jacket on the back of the door, and glanced down at the metal cot bed beneath the window.

'I suppose this will have to be mine,' he mumbled.

'I'll have that if you like,' said Heather. 'I really don't mind. I can sleep on a tree branch if necessary.'

'No,' Robert glanced up, suddenly. 'It's all right. I'm happy in this thing; you can have the other bed.' He turned to Sarah. 'Look, I got us a good deal with the old girl downstairs, so don't blow it. We may all have to share the same room but it's a good size. You know we have to be careful with our money if it's going to last the holiday.'

'Some holiday,' said Sarah. 'Back-packing and climbing in the wildest part of Ireland. All we seem to have done is walk.'

Suddenly there was a gentle knock on the door. It was so unexpected that the three of them fell silent and stared at one another blankly. Slowly, the door was opened and a small woman dressed in black, her hair tied into a bun, stepped into the room.

'Oh, I'm sorry,' she said. 'I thought perhaps you'd all taken a stroll. Welcome. Here now, nobody's been in this room in a long time. Few travellers visit the inn, especially at this time. Here, let me open the windows for you – air the place, blow away the old cobwebs, eh? That's the thing.'

The woman opened a pair of paint-blistered frames. The inn overlooked the village square. Outside, the hum of passing people floated up to them. She tucked in the corners of the two proper beds, and then turned down the sheets.

'On a walking holiday, you say?' she said to nobody in particular. 'I think it's good to see young people take the air and to be able to share like this. That's a grand thing. It's so good to have you here at a time like this.'

Robert was about to reply when another sound, something oddly familiar, drifted past the window. It was the pipes he had heard earlier, but this time they sounded more distinct, sharper and nearer too, and this time they all heard them.

'What are they?' he asked.

The woman ignored his question. Instead, she took some towels out of a cupboard and folded them across a rail beside the small porcelain sink.

'Those pipes, or flutes, what are they, please?' said Robert again.

'Oh, the pipes?' she laughed. 'Pay them no mind. It's a little custom we have, and you've arrived on the eve.'

'Who's playing them?' Sarah asked, as she started to unpack.

'And where?' said Heather. 'They sound as though they're everywhere.'

The woman smiled and shook out one of the towels. 'Oh, they're played here and there, mostly by the older women of the town. It's a custom, like I said. Sometimes they go up on the northern hillside and sit and play. It's been going on all week. It stops after tonight.' For a moment she stood in silence and watched the three of them. It was as if she were waiting. She coughed. 'Say, young lady – do you need anything washing?'

Sarah had pulled a dirty shirt from her bag. On the back was the outline of a goat. Robert had given one to each of them.

'There's no need,' she began.

The woman took the shirt and started to sing to herself, something Irish and folksy. Suddenly she froze and glanced at Sarah. She was unsmiling. 'You're a pretty young thing! Do you dance?'

Sarah tried to warm to the woman, but for some reason a cold sliver of unreasoned fear crept beneath her skin.

'Yes, yes, I do actually,' said Sarah stiffly.

'Good, good,' said the woman with a smile. 'It's a fine thing to dance. We end up with a right old time. They've been making the music for her, it's all for her. She'll be there.'

Robert tipped his bag on to the bed. A similar shirt to Sarah's fell out. The woman saw it.

'My, oh my,' said the woman. 'There's another. I'll have me a collection. It's a pretty thing, here.'

'It's our climbing club symbol,' said Sarah. Before he could say anything, the woman had grabbed the shirt and held it with the other.

'I bet you have one too?' She held Heather with a gaze of stone. Heather swallowed.

'No,' she said.

'You have so,' said Sarah sharply.

Heather gripped her bag. She did not know why, but she didn't want to give her shirt to this woman.

The woman glared.

'You can wash mine, by all means,' said Robert with a snort.

All of a sudden a surly red-faced man with mutton-chop whiskers and a white apron appeared at the door. His eyes were harder than stone and for a moment he glared at the woman.

'You're wanted downstairs, mother,' he said. 'The little one's crying for you. I'm sure these folks can manage.'

The three of them walked through the village, and they walked together. Over the past week they had separated amongst the hills, each climbing a favourite peak and calling to the others, but not here, not in the village high street.

'Is it me,' said Heather, 'or are they watching us?'

Robert said nothing. Sarah remained tight-lipped too. Their mid-afternoon stroll had turned into something slightly less pleasant. Nobody was aggressive, but nobody seemed friendly either. People stood in doorways and watched in silence as they passed. Sometimes a conversation would stop mid-sentence, and an eyebrow would rise. Robert nodded politely.

'Have you noticed?' asked Heather.

'Noticed what?' Robert replied.

'It's very busy. Strangely it's very busy. And look at some of the locals, they seem so old.'

Robert hadn't noticed this before, but she was right. There were a lot of older-looking people around, many standing on corners, simply standing and staring.

'Over there,' whispered Sarah, nodding in the direction of a courtyard. 'Look at those women.'

Robert and Heather followed her gaze. Beside another inn was an open courtyard. Washing lines were strung across the yard and half a dozen women or more were hanging out clothes.

'Must be laundry day,' said Robert.

'No, no, it's not right,' said Heather. 'I can't place it exactly.'

They stopped walking. 'I mean,' continued Heather, 'there's stacks of clothes, piles of them. Look at those baskets.' Further lines of women were gathering in the square now, and were hanging out shirts, trousers and skirts.

As they walked on, Robert glanced down a narrow side turning. Washing lines had been run from the upper storeys of the houses, above the street. Women were busy hanging clothes on these lines, which were already sagging from the weight.

'Perhaps it's just a clean village. That old girl was keen to get her hands on our shirts,' said Sarah as she popped a piece of gum into her mouth. 'Perhaps they all have dirty jobs.' She almost laughed, but Heather did not.

All of a sudden, the pipes started up again. A low wind blew through the village street; people almost stepped to one side to allow it through. But intertwined with the tuneless melody was a voice. There was no doubt this time: a cry, almost a wail. The people around them stopped and glanced upwards, as if expecting something more. The voice died with the wind as the sounds of the pipes grew louder.

Then Robert noticed the women. Several crossed themselves, and some kissed crucifixes which they wore around their necks.

Heather tugged at Robert's sleeve. He glanced down at her and put a finger to his lips. The level of the music lowered; unmistakably this time it came from the surrounding hills.

'I think I'd like to go back to the inn,' said Heather. Sarah gazed beyond the hillside.

As they walked back to the inn, the pipes cried out above the village. They sounded like strange birds, competing somehow with themselves. Now there seemed more of them. No longer a barely pretty tune, trills clashed against lower notes and there seemed to be no escape from the growing cacophony. Somewhere within, once again a voice was struggling to be heard.

Even Sarah seemed nervous and was uncharacteristically silent. As the three of them turned the corner which led to the inn, they passed a small track road to the left. Here, more women carried baskets of washing; and almost with urgency, more washing lines were being stretched across the road. But what stopped Robert in his tracks was the view beyond. The road led through to a gorse patch which led up the hillside. Sitting beside a rock, a little way up, was what seemed to be an old woman. She was bent almost double, and was dressed in a long sackcloth robe like a monk's. It was impossible to see her face, which was hidden in a hood, but bunches of her hair, wild and long, stretched down in front of her. Her hair was the darkest, deepest red. Bony fingers were close to her face, as though she were calling. Behind her, the sun was setting. The rays bled through the strands of wispy cloud like veins.

For some reason, Robert whispered, 'My God.'

He looked away for a second, and when he looked back she was gone.

'Visitors, travellers?' said a voice from out of nowhere.

Heather spun round. In the shadows of a doorway stood a grey-bearded figure. It was a man, who sucked on a hooked pipe. One eye was half closed.

'Travellers, I said?'

'Yes,' replied Heather. 'Yes, that's right.'

He grinned. Then he added, 'Do you dance?'

Sarah laughed. The music of the pipes crept from the hills again.

'Come on, girl, answer me question, do you dance?'

She grinned and twirled for him.

This time Heather did not reply. Robert hurried them on. Something glinted in Sarah's eye. For some reason, the music had begun to appeal.

The pipes continued into nightfall. Sarah tossed and tied herself up into her sheets. Heather lay awake staring at the ceiling, saying nothing, but her fingers made a claw and dug into the bed clothes. Robert felt strangely drowsy. There were occasions when the whistling melody melted into a cry, and it grew and ascended as though it were a bird climbing and climbing into the darker, more secret parts of the sky. It was hypnotic.

Heather got up and walked to the rear window. It looked out into the courtyard. The woman who had shown them to their room was joined by others. She was laying out two white shirts on a bush. But then, another villager lifted a small bucket containing a dark liquid which reflected the moonlight, and poured it on the shirts. Heather narrowed her eyes; she wondered what was going on. But then she saw what had filled the bucket. Nearby, two black cocks lay on a wooden table beside what looked like a butcher's chopper. She caught her breath and looked away.

'What . . . what are they doing?' she whispered.

The sound of the pipes grew.

'I can't stand it, why don't they shut up!' yelled Sarah suddenly. She sat up and put her face in her hands.

Within moments she had bounded out of bed and crossed the room.

'Where, where are you going?' asked Heather.

'Out. The bathroom. I don't know, I just need to get up, move around.' With that, she left the room, closing the door behind her.

'I'll see that she's all right,' said Heather.

The music of the pipes floated into Robert's head, but now the cries were more insistent. Perhaps there was really no music, only cries. Time passed. He was knocked from his semi-dream by a scratching noise. It was quite distinct, like nails on a board. It repeated itself, a straight, precise grating.

For a moment he wondered if there was a mouse, or worse still perhaps a rat, in the room. Shapes appeared to flicker on the ceiling. Was there something going on outside?

He looked across to the floor. The silvery beams of the moon threw a dark huddled shadow on to the polished bedroom boards. He instinctively looked up at the window above him. There was something pressed against the glass. It was only after a moment that he realized it was a face. It was huge and fierce, a woman's face with folded creases of flesh within which were eyes that shone with a white marble blankness. Her blood-red hair billowed behind her as though she might be floating there, in space. Her mouth was a dark cavern, and her tongue lolled like a bloated worm. A hand of thin spindly fingers scratched down the glass. But it was her cry that drowned out everything else. It was the cry he thought he had heard before, that mingled with the pipes; but this time it was a wail, alone, a pure scream from the bottom of an abyss.

Robert sat upright with a shudder which shook his bones. A coldness he had never felt before rippled through his flesh.

The pipes were everywhere. Outside, in the street below, came the sounds of people. There were cries, whoops of joy, screams. He rolled out of his cot and looked back at the window. There was nobody there. Hesitating at first, he moved forward to peer out. Had he been dreaming, he wondered? But the scene below now occupied his thoughts. There were crowds of them, villagers. They were a mixture of young and old, but the staggering ungainly gait showed him that most of the figures were elderly – almost ancient. And they were dancing. They made a grotesque line, weaving and swaying. There was something about the way they moved which bothered him deeply. The faces glowed with a gleam of madness.

Then he saw Heather.

She was in the centre of a ring of villagers which had formed close by the line of dancers. She was screaming, her hands holding the sides of her face as though she was grappling with the wind. The bouncing chain of people held something like rags above their heads, waving them as if they were grotesque banners. The light of the moon glistened on the whiteness of the rags. There were marks, streaks of something wet which glistened beneath the silvery rays of the moon. He swallowed hard as he realized what it was: an awful brownish red wash of colour. A blonde-haired girl, daubed with the same wash, led the chain. The laugh was unmistakeable. It was Sarah.

Robert rushed out of the room. In the tap room downstairs, villagers were heaving their bones to the

music of the pipes, stepping to the terrible music. They seemed not to see him as he pushed past them. It was not until he stood in the doorway that all became clearer. Twisting and turning within the dancers, like a flickering shadow, was a red-haired woman. She held pieces of rags above her head – almost in triumph. It was the face at the window.

He staggered back. Droplets, like generous beads of sweat, dripped from the dancers to the floor to make pools of blood. It was almost a dance of death. Then he saw the woman from the inn. Triumphantly she swept into the dancers and carried a shirt; it was another similar to the one the red-haired woman had held in her claws, but this time there was something about the garment which identified it: an image on the back – *like the outline of a goat*. She looked at him for seconds only. She gave it to the red-haired woman who tore at it with glee. With a groan he realized who the shirts had belonged to.

He cried and rushed forward, grabbing Sarah by the hand. She was somewhere else, in a grim place of **reverie**; and her mouth was wild and open. He yanked her behind him as he forced his way through the ring, and caught Heather by the waist.

With tears in his eyes, he ran and ran and ran from that place, the two girls beside him. He ran until the sounds of the pipes, the cries, and the screams could be heard no longer. Together they walked to the next village and arrived at sunrise, in silence.

Later the next day, as they waited for the ferry, Robert was told the story. He heard it from an old boy – a man of the road – in exchange for a few coins. He said they should never have been in Holihook that night. For Holihook had long been a community in the grip of a Banshee, who once a year foretold the deaths that were due to the families there. Usually, the Banshee would wash the clothes of those about to die, and hang them out to dry. But the villagers now filled all of the washing lines themselves with their own washing, denying the Banshee. To **appease** the Banshee, they would prepare for the dance, and the music that would drown out her

---

reverie: dream, imagination
appease: pacify

voice. Nobody would die that year if nobody heard her summoning cries, and if she was unable to wash their clothes.

But sometimes, just sometimes, the old man had said, they would let her have items of travellers' clothing if any visited their village. They would ritually bury the clothes in the earth, and wash them by moonlight in the blood of two black cocks. This would transfer the foretold deaths to the unwary travellers. Then he had laughed. 'It's only a story,' he said.

The three of them never spoke of the events.

Something had happened that had placed distance between them. Heather became quieter still and rarely climbed, and Robert was easily startled by the innocent flap of washing on a windy day. But Sarah continued to bear that smile, as though now she had her secret.

It was not until much later that year whilst climbing with their club on a challenging rock face, that Robert remembered and realized. He had heard the cry of the thing at the window, and the Banshee had handled and torn at their shirts.

The accident was horrific. As Sarah and Robert plunged off the mountain face, grotesquely clawing and dancing in the wind as they fell, he heard the pipes once again.

Out of the Everywhere
Marilyn Watts

It came in the night. Suddenly there was another being in the house, and we caught our breath and stared. Silence at first, and then its closed face opened and it screamed. But not at us.

The sound was terrifying. I looked to the window, but there was nothing – no movement, no noise outside. Beyond the door, nothing stirred. Everywhere still and yet it was here. Its scream cut through the air, like no sound I had ever heard before. Certainly no human sound – cat-like if anything, but fuller and more eerie, more piercing. A scream of anger and rage, of pain and surprise, for where it found itself.

At the turn of the night, when dark blue thinned to a glimmer in the sky, it opened its eyes. It must have opened its eyes to the sky first because when finally it swivelled its head we saw the dark night-sky colour of its eyes gazing at us. Perhaps it brought nothing with it but took everything from this new world in which it had arrived.

So it looked at us with its night eyes, out of its wrinkled, wise face, and seemed to know everything there was to know.

Yet it needed help. It needed something to cover it against the coolness. When we brought a blanket, it quietened. And when we held it, it seemed content. It writhed for a while, then closed those strange deep eyes, and it was as though the shutters had come down. It didn't so much go to sleep as go away. Its body was still here, slumped and curled as a kitten, but its being was elsewhere.

I looked at it, lying like an island in the middle of my world, and wondered where it had gone to, when it would come back. And although it couldn't hear me, or understand our language, I whispered into the whirl at the side of its head.

So what to do? We told our friends about it, of course, and soon a constant stream of people arrived, nosy and noisy, with their questions and comments. And cameras. They brought exclamations of surprise and amazement, and left with the efforts of trying to capture it on film. Because it was unique – the camera was the only way they had to take a part of it with them. The creature stared at them and bore the bright flashes calmly. If these strange people and their little machines didn't harm it, then they could be tolerated. Eventually it would close its eyes against the lights and drift off into another world inside its head where no one could reach it.

Sometimes at night I would wake, with no reason and no idea why I had done so. Some instinct, some calling perhaps that humans don't usually hear. And I would tiptoe down the hallway and into the end room. It slept there, so quietly. I would wet my fingers and hold them in front of the holes in its face, and feel the little winds blow in and out, and know that it was still with us. And beyond the window the sky was dark, and all the little dots of stars shone through the winter branches of the tree, and the great big obvious moon flooded light into the garden and I would wonder, why here? Why us?

It knew very little about us in some ways, and then I would look into those dark eyes and know, without doubt, that it knew everything. That it had arrived in our world knowing everything that was important.

But the basic, day-to-day things, the tasks to survive, we had to teach it ourselves. It would watch us and copy, its odd face mimicking our expressions, its dumpy body trying hopelessly to move in the way we did. It learnt to eat and drink, to force food into that moving hole in its face. It learnt to reach out for things, and examine them – to work out what different objects could do and what they were good for. It would taste them, sniff, turn them over and over, watching all the time.

Sometimes I thought it might even understand us. We had no idea of its own language, of course, so it taught us that at the same time as we taught it ours. We learnt a bit about what its different sounds meant, but a lot of its communication was done with body and face. Eventually we learnt when it was happy or sad, frightened or calm. It was all we could understand.

But it couldn't last. Nothing so strange ever does. Separate beings, distinct races, can never live together as such for long. One must triumph in the end. It is not human nature to allow separateness for ever. The old human instincts rose up: to destroy, to know, to make like us.

And in a way it lost. The little thing. It had to. After all, it had come to depend on us for food, for shelter, even for company. How do you subject another race? You make them dress like you, eat your food, obey your rules. And ultimately you teach them your language, and tell them that that is right, that is how they must communicate. And it was like that with this creature. It was the only way we could live with it, and so we went ahead and made it to be one of us.

Deep inside it, I know, there may still be a core that is other. Even now, sometimes, when I look at its eyes (which have changed, by the way – they are lighter and a normal blue-grey and no longer know everything), when I catch a look that I cannot understand, it occurs to me that I have not won. Not fully. But nearly. Nearly. Because eventually it gave in and **acquiesced**. It took time. The world had turned round to summer again. And the sun was bright and sharp the day it toddled towards me, having learnt human walking; and held out its arms, having been taught to need a human caress; and said 'Mummy'.

---

acquiesced: conformed

The Breadwinner
Leslie Halward

The parents of a boy of fourteen were waiting for him to come home with his first week's wages.

The mother had laid the table and was cutting some slices of bread and butter for tea. She was a little woman with a pinched face and a spare body, dressed in a blue blouse and skirt, the front of the skirt covered with a starched white apron. She looked tired and frequently sighed heavily.

The father, sprawling inelegantly in an old armchair by the fireside, legs outstretched, was little too. He had watery blue eyes and a heavy brown moustache, which he sucked occasionally.

These people were plainly poor, for the room, though clean, was meanly furnished, and the thick pieces of bread and butter were the only food on the table.

As she prepared the meal, the woman from time to time looked contemptuously at her husband. He ignored her, raising his eyebrows, humming or tapping his teeth now and then with his finger-nails, making a pretence of being profoundly bored.

'You'll keep your hands off the money,' said the woman, obviously repeating something that she had already said several times before. 'I know what'll happen to it if you get hold of it. He'll give it to me. It'll pay the rent and buy us a bit of food, and not go into the till at the nearest public-house.'

'You shut your mouth,' said the man quietly.

'I'll not shut my mouth!' cried the woman, in a quick burst of anger. 'Why should I shut my mouth? You've been boss here for long enough. I put up with it when you were bringing money into the house, but I'll not put up with it now. You're nobody here. Understand? *Nobody*. I'm boss and he'll hand the money to me!'

'We'll see about that,' said the man, leisurely poking the fire.

Nothing more was said for about five minutes.

Then the boy came in. He did not look older than ten or eleven years. He looked absurd in long trousers. The whites of his eyes against his black face gave him a startled expression.

The father got to his feet.

'Where's the money?' he demanded.

The boy looked from one to the other. He was afraid of his father. He licked his pale lips.

'Come on now,' said the man. 'Where's the money?'

'Don't give it to him,' said the woman. 'Don't give it to him, Billy. Give it to me.'

The father advanced on the boy, his teeth showing in a snarl under his big moustache.

'Where's the money?' he almost whispered.

The boy looked him straight in the eyes.

'I lost it,' he said.

'You – *what*?' cried his father.

'I lost it,' the boy repeated.

The man began to shout and wave his hands about.

'Lost it! *Lost it*! What are you talking about? How could you lose it?'

'It was in a packet,' said the boy, 'a little envelope. I lost it.'

'Where did you lose it?'

'I don't know. I must have dropped it in the street.'

'Did you go back and look for it?'

The boy nodded. 'I couldn't find it,' he said.

The man made a noise in his throat, half grunt, half moan – the sort of noise that an animal would make.

'So you lost it, did you?' he said. He stepped back a

couple of paces and took off his belt – a wide, thick belt with a heavy brass buckle. 'Come here,' he said.

The boy, biting his lower lip so as to keep back the tears, advanced, and the man raised his arm. The woman, motionless until that moment, leapt forward and seized it. Her husband, finding strength in his blind rage, pushed her aside easily. He brought the belt down on the boy's back. He beat him unmercifully about the body and legs. The boy sank to the floor, but did not cry out.

When the man had spent himself, he put on the belt and pulled the boy to his feet.

'Now you'll get off to bed,' he said.

'The lad wants some food,' said the woman.

'He'll go to bed. Go and wash yourself.'

Without a word the boy went into the scullery and washed his hands and face. When he had done this he went straight upstairs.

The man sat down at the table, ate some bread and butter and drank two cups of tea. The woman ate nothing. She sat opposite him, never taking her eyes from his face, looking with hatred at him. Just as before, he took no notice of her, ignored her, behaved as if she were not there at all.

When he finished the meal he went out.

Immediately he had shut the door the woman jumped to her feet and ran upstairs to the boy's room.

He was sobbing bitterly, his face buried in the pillow. She sat on the edge of the bed and put her arms about him, pressed him close to her breast, ran her fingers through his disordered hair, whispered endearments, consoling him. He let her do this, finding comfort in her caresses, relief in his own tears.

After a while the weeping ceased. He raised his head and smiled at her, his wet eyes bright. Then he put his hand under his pillow and withdrew a small dirty envelope.

'Here's the money,' he whispered.

She took the envelope and opened it and pulled out a long strip of a paper with some figures on it – a ten shilling note and a sixpence.

Fabric Crafts
Anne Fine

Alastair MacIntyre gripped his son Blair by the throat and shook him till his eyes bulged.

'Look here, laddie,' he hissed. 'I'm warning ye. One more time, say that one more time and whatever it is ye think ye're so good at, *whatever*, I'll have ye prove it!'

'You let go of Blair at once,' said Helen MacIntyre. 'His breakfast's getting cold on the table.'

Giving his son one last fierce shake, Alastair MacIntrye let go. Blair staggered backwards and caught his head against the spice shelf. Two or three little jars toppled over and the last of the turmeric puffed off the shelf and settled gently on his dark hair.

Alastair MacIntyre heard the crack of his son's head against the wood and looked up in anguish.

'Did ye hear that? Did ye hear that, Helen? He banged his head on yon shelf. He couldnae have done that a week back. The laddie's still growing! It'll be new trousers in another month. Och, I cannae bear it, Helen! I cannae bear to watch him sprouting out of a month's wages in clothes before my eyes. I'd raither watch breakfast telly!'

And picking up his plate, he left the room.

'What was all that about?' Blair asked his mother, rubbing his head. 'Why did he go berserk? What happened?'

'You said it again.'

'I didnae!'

'You did.'

'How? When?'

'You came downstairs, walked through the door, came up behind me at the stove, looked over my shoulder at the bacon in the pan and you said it.'

'I didnae!'

'You did, lamb. You said: "I bet I could fit more slices of bacon into the pan that that." That's what you said. That's when he threw himself across the kitchen to throttle you.'

'I didnae hear myself.'

Helen MacIntyre put her hands on her son's shoulders and raised herself on to her tiptoes. She tried to blow the turmeric off his hair, but she wasn't tall enough.

'No. You don't hear yourself. And you don't think before you speak either. I reckon all your fine brains are draining away into your legs.'

'Blair doesnae have any brains.' Blair's younger sister, Annie, looked up from her crunchy granola. 'If he had any brains, he wouldnae say the things he does.'

'I dinnae say them,' Blair argued, fitting his long legs awkwardly under the table. 'They just come out. I dinnae even hear them when they're said!'

'There you are,' Annie crowed. 'That's what Mum said. All legs, no brain.'

She pushed her plate away across the table and dumped her school bag in its place. 'Tuesday. Have I got everything I need? Swimsuit, gymshorts, metalwork goggles, flute and embroidery.'

'Wheesht!' Blair warned. 'Keep your voice down.' But it was too late. The cheery litany had brought Alastair MacIntyre back into the doorway like the dark avenging angel of some ancient, long-forgotten educational system.

'Are ye quite sure ye've no forgotten anything?' he asked his daughter with bitter sarcasm. 'Skis? Sunglasses? Archery set? Saddle and bridle, perhaps?'

'Och, no!' said Annie. 'I won't be needing any of them till it's our class's turn to go to Loch Tay.'

Alastair MacIntyre turned to his son.

'What about you, laddie? Are you all packed and ready

for a long day in school? Climbing boots? Beekeeping gear? Snorkel and oxygen tank?'

'Tuesday,' mused Blair. 'Only fabric crafts.'

'Fabric crafts?'

'You know,' his wife explained to him. 'Sewing. That useful little skill you never learned.'

'Sewing? A laddie of mine sitting at his desk sewing?'

'Och, no Dad. We dinnae sit at our desks. We have to share the silks and cottons. We sit round in a circle, and chat.'

'Sit in a circle and sew and chat?'

Blair backed away.

'Mam, he's turning rare red. I hope he's no' going to try again to strangle me!'

Alastair MacIntyre put his head in his hands.

'I cannae believe it,' he said in broken tones. 'My ain laddie, the son and grandson of miners, sits in a sewing circle and chats.'

'I dinnae just chat. I'm very good. I've started on embroidery now I've finished hemming my apron!'

Alastair MacIntyre groaned.

'His apron!'

'Dinnae take on so,' Helen MacIntyre comforted her husband. 'Everyone's son does it. The times are changing.' She tipped a pile of greasy dishes into the sink and added: 'Thank God.'

'Not my son!' Alastair MacIntyre cried. 'Not my son! Not embroidery! No! I cannae bear it! I'm a reasonable man. I think I move with the times as fast as the next man. I didnae make a fuss when my ain lassie took up the metalwork. I didnae like it, but I bore with it. But there are limits. A man must have his sticking place, and this is mine. I willnae have my one and only son doing embroidery.'

'Why not?' demanded Blair. 'I'm very good at it. I bet I can embroider much, much better than wee Annie here.'

A terrible silence fell. Then Annie said:

'Ye said it again!'

Blair's eyes widened in horror.

'I didnae!'

'You did. We all heard ye. You said: "I bet I can embroider much, much better than wee Annie here".'

'I didnae!'

'Ye did!'

'Mam?'

Mrs MacIntyre reached up and laid a comforting hand on his shoulder.

'Ye did, lamb. I'm sorry. I heard it, too.'

Suddenly Alastair MacIntyre looked as if an unpleasant thought had just struck him. He quickly recovered himself and began to whistle casually. He reached over to the draining board and picked up his lunch box. He slid his jacket off the peg behind the door, gave his wife a surreptitious little kiss on the cheek and started sidling towards the back door.

'*Dad*!'

Alastair MacIntyre pretended not to have heard.

'Hey, Dad!'

Even a deaf man would have felt the reverberations. Alastair MacIntyre admitted defeat. He turned back to his daughter.

'Yes, hen?'

'What about what you told him?'

'Who?'

'Blair.'

'What about, hen?'

'About what would happen if he said it again.'

Alastair MacIntyre looked like a hunted animal. He loosened his tie and cleared his throat, and still his voice came out all ragged.

'What did I say?'

'You said: "Say that one more time and whatever it is

you think you're so good at, *whatever*, I'll have ye prove it." That's what you said.'

'Och, weel. This doesnae count. The laddie cannae prove he sews better than you.'

'Why not?'

'He just cannae.'

'He can, too. I'm entering my embroidery for the end-of-term competition. He can enter his.'

'No, lassie!'

'Yes, Dad. You said so.'

'I was only joking.'

'Dad! You were not!'

Alastair MacIntyre ran his finger around his collar to loosen it, and looked towards his wife for rescue.

'Helen?'

Annie folded her arms over her school bag and looked towards her mother for justice.

'Mam?'

Mrs MacIntyre turned away and slid her arms, as she'd done every morning for the last nineteen years, into the greasy washing-up water.

'I think,' she said, 'it would be very good for him.'

Alastair MacIntyre stared in sheer disbelief at his wife's back. Then he slammed out. The heavy shudder of the door against the wooden frame dislodged loose plaster from the ceiling. Most of it fell on Blair, mingling quite nicely with the turmeric.

'Good for me, nothing,' said Blair. 'I'd enjoy it.'

'I didnae mean good for you,' admitted Mrs MacIntyre. 'I meant it would be good for your father.'

It was with the heaviest of hearts that Alastair MacIntyre returned from the pithead that evening to find his son perched on the doorstep, a small round embroidery frame in one hand, a needle in the other, mastering stem stitch.

'Have ye no' got anything better to do?' he asked his son irritably.

Blair turned his work over and bit off a loose end with practised ease.

'Och, Dad. Ye know I've only got a week. I'm going to have to work night and day as it is.'

Alastair MacIntyre took refuge in the kitchen. To try to cheer himself, he said to Helen:

'Wait till his friends drap in to find him ta'en up wi' yon rubbish. They'll take a rise o' the laddie that will bring him back into his senses.'

'Jimmy and Iain were here already. He sent them along to The Work Box on Pitlochrie Street to buy another skein of Flaming Orange so he could finish off his border of french knots.'

The tea mug shook in Alastair MacIntyre's hand.

'Och, no,' he whispered.

Abandoning his tea, he strode back into the hall, only to find his son and friends blocking the doorway as they held one skein of coloured embroidery floss after another up to the light.

'Ye cannae say that doesnae match. That's perfect, that is.'

'Ye maun be half blind! It's got a heap more red in it than the other.'

'It has not. It's as yellowy as the one he's run out of.'

'It is not.'

'What about that green, then? That's perfect, right?'

'Aye, that's **unco' guid**, that match.'

'Aye.'

Clutching his head, Alastair MacIntyre retreated.

The next day, Saturday, he felt better. Ensconced in his armchair in front of the rugby international on the television, his son at his side, he felt a happy man again – till he looked round.

---

unco' guid: uncommonly good

Blair sat with his head down, stitching away with a rather fetching combination of Nectarine and Baby Blue.

'Will ye no' watch the match?' Alastair MacIntyre snapped at his son.

'I am watching,' said Blair. 'You should try watching telly and doing satin stitch. It's no' the easiest thing.'

Alastair MacInyre tried to put it all out of his mind. France vs Scotland was not a match to spoil with parental disquiet. And when, in the last few moments, the beefy fullback from Dunfermline converted the try that saved Scotland's bacon, he bounced in triumph on the springs of his chair and shouted in his joy:

'Och, did ye see that? Did ye see that!'

'Sorry,' said Blair. 'This coral stitch is the very de'il. Ye cannae simply stop and look up halfway through.'

All through the night, Alastair MacIntyre brooded. He brooded through his Sunday breakfast and brooded

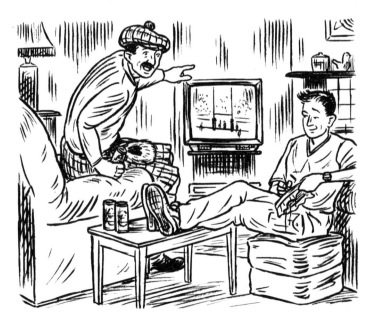

through his Sunday lunch. He brooded all through an afternoon's gardening and through most of supper. Then, over a second helping of prunes, he finally hatched out a plan.

The next evening, when he drove home from the pithead, instead of putting the car – a K-registration Temptress – away in the garage he parked it in front of the house and went in search of his wayward son. He found him on the upstairs landing, fretting to Annie about whether his cross stitches were correctly aligned.

'Lay off that, laddie,' Alastair MacIntyre wheedled. 'Come out and help me tune up the car engine.'

Blair appeared not to have heard. He held his work up for his father's inspection.

'What do you reckon?' he said. 'Be honest. Dinnae spare my feelings. Do ye think those stitches in the China Blue are entirely regular? Now look very closely. I want ye to be **picky**.'

Alastair MacIntyre shuddered. Was this his son? He felt as if an **incubus** had taken hold of his first born.

'Blair,' he pleaded. 'Come out to the car. I need your help.'

'Take wee Annie,' Blair told him. 'She'll help ye. She got top marks in the car maintenance module. I cannae come.'

'Please, laddie.'

Alastair MacIntyre was almost in tears.

Blair rose. Extended to his full height, he towered over his father.

'Dad,' he said. 'Take wee Annie. I cannae come. I cannae risk getting oil ingrained in my fingers. It'll ruin my work.'

Barely stifling his sob of humiliation and outrage,

picky: critical
incubus: evil spirit

Alastair MacIntyre took the stairs three at a time on his way down and out to the nearest dark pub.

He came home to find wee Annie leaning over his engine, wiping her filthy hands on an oily rag.

'Ye've no' been looking after it all well,' she scolded him. 'Your sparking plugs were a disgrace. And how long is it since you changed the oil, I'd like to know.'

Mortified, feeling a man among Martians, Alastair MacIntyre slunk through his own front door and up to his bed.

On the morning of the school prize-giving, Alastair MacIntyre woke feeling sick. He got no sympathy from his wife, who laid his suit out on the double bed.

Alastair MacIntyre put his head in his hands.

'I cannae bear it!' he said. 'I cannae bear it. My ain son, winning first prize for fabric crafts for his sewing! I tell you, Helen. I cannae bear it!'

He was still muttering 'I cannae bear it' over and over to himself as the assistant head teacher ushered the two of them to their seats in the crowded school hall. The assistant head teacher patted him on the back in an encouraging fashion and told him: 'You maun be a very proud man today, Mr MacIntyre.'

Alastair MacIntyre sank onto his seat, close to tears.

He kept his eyes closed for most of the ceremony, opening them only when Annie was presented with the Junior Metalwork Prize, a new rasp. Here, to prove he was as much a man of the times as the next fellow, he clapped loudly and enthusiastically, then shut his eyes again directly, for fear of seeing his only son presented with a new pack of needles.

When the moment of truth came, he cracked and peeped. Surreptitiously he peered around at the other parents. Nobody was chortling. Nobody was whispering contemptuously to a neighbour. Nobody was so much as snickering quietly up a sleeve. So when everyone else clapped, he clapped too, so as not to seem churlish.

Somebody leaned forward from the row behind and tapped on his shoulder.

'I wadna say but what ye maun be a proud faither today, Alastair MacIntyre.'

And raw as he was, he could discern no trace of sarcasm in the remark.

As they filed out of the hall, Annie and Blair rejoined them. Alastair MacIntyre congratulated his daughter. He tried to follow up this success by congratulating his son, but the words stuck in his throat. He was rescued by the arrival, in shorts and shirts, of most of the school football team.

'Blair! Are ye no' ready yet? We're waitin' on ye!'

The goalie, a huge burly lad whose father worked at the coal face at Alastair MacIntyre's pit, suddenly reached forward and snatched at Blair's embroidery. Blair's father shuddered. But all the goalie did was to fold it up neatly.

'A fair piece o' work, that,' he said. 'I saw it on display in yon hall. I dinnae ken how ye managed all them fiddly bits.'

'Och, it was nothing,' said Blair. 'I bet if you tried, you could do one just as guid.'

Alastair MacIntyre stared at his son, then his wife, then his daughter, then his son again.

'No, no,' demurred the goalie. 'I couldnae manage that. I've no' got your colour sense.'

He handed the embroidery to Alastair MacIntyre.

'Will ye keep hold o' that for him,' he said. 'He's got to come and play football now. We cannae wait any longer.' He turned to Annie. 'And you'll have to come too, wee Annie. Neil's awa' sick. You'll have to be the referee.'

Before she ran off, Annie dropped her new rasp into one of her father's pockets. Blair dropped a little packet into the other.

Alastair MacIntyre jumped as if scalded.

'What's in there?' he demanded, afraid to reach in and touch it in case it was a darning mushroom, or a new thimble.

'Iron-on letters,' Blair said. 'I asked for them. They're just the job for football shirts. We learned to iron in home economics. I'm going to fit up the whole football team.'

'What with?'

'KIRKCALDIE KILLERS,' Blair told him proudly. 'In Flaming Orange and Baby Blue.'

Hobbyist
Fredric Brown

'I heard a rumour,' Sangstrom said, 'to the effect that you – ' He turned his head and looked about him to make absolutely sure that he and the druggist were alone in the tiny prescription pharmacy. The druggist was a gnomelike gnarled little man who could have been any age from fifty to a hundred. They were alone, but Sangstrom dropped his voice just the same. ' – to the effect that you have a completely undetectable poison.'

The druggist nodded. He came around the counter and locked the front door of the shop, then walked toward a doorway behind the counter. 'I was about to take a coffee break,' he said. 'Come with me and have a cup.'

Sangstrom followed him around the counter and through the doorway to a back room ringed by shelves of bottles from floor to ceiling. The druggist plugged in an electric percolator, found two cups and put them on a table that had a chair on either side of it. He motioned Sangstrom to one of the chairs and took the other himself. 'Now,' he said. 'Tell me. Whom do you want to kill, and why?'

'Does it matter?' Sangstrom asked. 'Isn't it enough that I pay for – '

The druggist interrupted him with an upraised hand. 'Yes, it matters. I must be convinced that you deserve what I can give you. Otherwise – ' he shrugged.

'All right,' Sangstrom said. 'The *whom* is my wife. The *why* – .' He started the long story. Before he had quite finished, the percolator had finished its task and the druggist briefly interrupted to get coffee for them. Sangstrom finished his story.

The little druggist nodded. 'Yes, I occasionally dispense an undetectable poison. I do so freely; I do not charge for it, if I think the case is deserving. I have helped many murderers.'

'Fine,' Sangstrom said. 'Please give it to me, then.'

The druggist smiled at him. 'I already have. By the time the coffee was ready I had decided that you deserved it. It was, as I said, free. But there is a price for the antidote.'

Sangstrom turned pale. But he had anticipated – not this, but the possibility of a double-cross or some form of blackmail. He pulled a pistol from his pocket.

The little druggist chuckled. 'You daren't use that. Can you find the antidote' – he waved at the shelves – 'among those thousands of bottles? Or would you find a faster more **virulent** poison? Or if you think I'm bluffing, that you are not really poisoned, go ahead and shoot. You'll know the answer within three hours when the poison starts to work.'

'How much for the antidote?' Sangstrom growled.

'Quite reasonable. A thousand dollars. After all, a man must live. Even if his hobby is preventing murders, there's no reason why he shouldn't make money at it, is there?'

Sangstrom growled and put the pistol down, but within reach, and took out his wallet. Maybe after he had the antidote, he'd still use that pistol. He counted out a thousand dollars in hundred-dollar bills and put it on the table.

The druggist made no immediate move to pick it up. He said: 'And one other thing – for your wife's safety and mine. You will write a confession of your intention – your former intention, I trust – to murder your wife. Then you will wait till I go out and mail it to a friend of mine on the

---

virulent: deadly

homicide detail. He'll keep it as evidence in case you ever *do* decide to kill your wife. Or me, for that matter.

'When that is in the mail it will be safe for me to return here and give you the antidote. I'll get you paper and pen . . . '

'Oh, one other thing – although I do not absolutely insist on it. Please help spread the word about my undetectable poison, will you? One never knows, Mr Sangstrom. The life you save, if you have any enemies, just might be your own.'

---

homicide detail: murder squad

A Price to Pay
Timothy Callender

He started from sleep in terror – and leapt up from the ground. For a moment he could not understand the noise, and he crouched there in the shadows with the whites of his eyes large in the darkness. Then he realized that the noise was the barking of dogs, and the shouts of the police. They knew where he was. The dragnet was closing in.

He looked around with a growing panic and a bleak despair knocking at his heart. He was in the shadow of the trees, but ahead of him, where he had to run, the beach stretched long and deserted in the starlight.

He could not remain in the shadows any longer, because, if he did, with the men and dogs closing in on him, there would be no possible chance of escape.

He stood up for a moment, and then began to run. His feet pounded through the loose powdery sand. He was very tired, because he had already run a long way and had had very little time to rest. Yet, there was no question of stopping, for, around him and coming closer all the time, was the circle of capture, and conviction, and death.

Now, to his left, he saw the first lights of the torches fingering through the trees. He was running closer to the edge of the sea now where the sand was firmer, and he doubled himself over and prayed that the lights would miss him. The trees were intercepting their search, and for the moment, he was safe. But now, to his right, where the trees thinned out and disappeared, he saw the dots of light wavering from spot to spot, and he knew that they were coming up from ahead of him also. Behind him, the barking of the dogs sounded even louder. How far behind? Three or four hundred yards? He could not tell.

The only opening was the sea. He thought of this with a sort of surprise that he hadn't thought of it before. Still running, he turned his head and saw the rocks, heard the seething of the water over the long low platform of sharp coral stretching submerged out into the dark. He hesitated, and, as he did so, a torch, clearing the trees, stabbed the darkness over his head and fell upon him, etching him out clearly against the backdrop of the white sea. 'Stop,' a voice shouted, and he froze in the glare of the light.

Then he turned, leapt out of the light, and plunged head first under the water, straightening out quickly so as to avoid disembowelling himself upon the ragged teeth of the reef. The waves surged around him and already his lungs were bursting and his ears were pounding, for he had been almost out of breath when he took the dive.

He came up out of the water behind a rock which shielded him from the glare of the torches and this afforded him a little breathing space. Further out to sea he could discern a large cluster of bigger rocks, and he felt that if he could only reach them, he would be relatively safe. He was gauging the distance towards the rocks when he heard voices, and he knew that the police were coming out into the sea, walking upon the platform of reef; and, as he looked, light gleamed whitely on the water, and jerked around from rock to rock, trying to spot him.

He took a deep long breath and plunged under the water again. Scraping his knees every now and then, he slowly worked his way towards the cluster, averaging his progress by the number of strokes he made. He surfaced again, and a beam of light skimmed over the spot where he had just come up. It was now moving away from him. He dived again. And now he reached one of the rocks that formed the cluster. He reached out and grabbed a sharp jutting portion of it. The insweeping waves threw him against it and bruised his body, bloodied his gripping hands, but he did not lose his hold. He remained there whilst fingers of light patterned their search upon the sea and the sky and the rocks, and he shivered from fright and fear that, after all, he might not be able to escape them.

Three thousand dollars, he thought. That was a lot of money. That was the price they'd set on his capture. A lot of people will be looking for me in the hope of getting that, he thought. Three thousand dollars!

He stiffened and looked up. Above the noise of the waves on the rock, he could distinguish men's voices. And now he could hear the scrabbling noise of someone clambering up on the rock. He drew in his breath and pressed his back against the jagged side of the rock, waiting, his eyes staring upward. The rock rose behind and above him as he gazed from its base upward to the top edge silhouetted against the dark blue of the sky. He saw a pair of heavy boots, black and sharp against the sky, descending. He held his breath more deeply and his fingers clawed upon the rock behind. There was a splash. The policeman had dropped upon the rock platform below, and staggered as he landed, the light of the torch dancing crazily around at the impact. And then . . . the torch dropped from his hand into the welter of the waves. The policeman was close to him, so close that he could touch him, but the torch was gone, and the policeman couldn't see in the overhanging darkness of the rock.

The policeman swore under his breath, then shouted 'Hi!'

'Hinds?' someone replied.

'Yeah. I loss my light, man.'

'You ain't see nothing?'

'Hell, I don't know where he could have gone. I thought I was in front of him. You think he gone back in the opposite direction?'

'He was running this way, man.'

'So the smart thing to do is to head the other way as soon as he get in the water . . .'

'You might be right. Hell, why I ain't think of that before?'

'Hold on. I coming up to you. This place dangerous, man. A man could slip off one o' these rocks and drown easy, easy.'

'Well, come up and lewwe go. We going have to wait till morning. We can't do nothing more now.'

The policeman scrambled up. The voices receded. The sea pounded on the rock as before.

The man waited for a few moments. Then he walked gingerly along the treacherous platform and slipped into the water. In the distance he could see faintly the retreating figures of the policemen. Under cover of the rocks, he headed for the shore. He swam warily, for the sharp teeth of the reef were not easy to avoid.

At last he reached the shore. The barking of the dogs had receded into the distance, and he ran along now, all caution gone.

'I don't want to have nothing to do with it,' his brother said. 'That is your own business. It was only a matter of time before this sort of thing happen. You was a blasted thief all your life, Franklyn, and now you reaping the rewards.'

'All right, Joe, I is a thief, yes, but that isn't mean I is to get hang for a thing I didn't do . . .'

'You trying to say you ain't kill her? Man, read the papers. You should see what they saying 'bout you. You up to your neck in trouble this time.'

'But, Joe, you got to help me. Blood thicker than water. You can't let them get me for a thing I ain't done.'

'Look. You may as well stop saying that,' his brother said. 'Read this.' And he threw a newspaper over to the hunted man, who took it and scanned it with terror-haunted eyes.

The headline said FORDE STILL HUNTED BY POLICE.

It told the world that he had killed a woman, and he had no chance to condemn or save himself.

Franklyn crumpled the paper into a ball, and threw it, in a sudden spasm of frustration, violence and fear, away from him.

'Everybody got Franklyn Forde class up as a murderer,' he groaned, 'and, Joe, I ain't do it. You believe me, Joe, ain't you?' His eyes searched his brother's face in hope, but Joe's eyes were cold and hard and his lips compressed.

'Listen, you fool,' Joe said, and suddenly his expression changed. Tears blurred his eyes, and he wiped them away brusquely. 'We grow up together, and you know how we mother try her best. And you had to turn out so. Time and time again I tell you was to behave yourself, 'cause after all, you is my little brother. But no, you won't listen.

And now you running away from a murder charge. And I ain't in no position to help you. The wife in the next room there sick. She sick bad bad. And I been seeing hell lately. The grocery bill over a hundred dollars now and the man say he ain't giving me no more credit. The children hungry. They gone school today without tasting a thing this morning. Look at the old house. Falling apart. I in enough trouble already, and now you can't find nowhere else but to run here. You want me to get you out o' the island. You only out to preserve your own life and you don't care what happen to me once you get 'way. The police can ketch me and lock me up, and it won't matter a dam to you.'

'That ain't true, I only axing for a break, Joe. You won't never have to worry 'bout me no more. And you got to understand it is a mistake. I ain't kill nobody. I ain't done nothing to die for.'

'You still lying?' Joe suddenly shouted. 'You insulting my sense with that stupid lie?'

'I ain't do it.' His voice was shrill with the need to be believed, to be believed if only for a moment. But his brother's face had resumed its former expression. It was like stone.

'I only went in the room to steal, I telling you. I search round and the woman sleeping on the bed. I ain't touch her. And then . . . I hear somebody else come in the room. The woman own husband. I had was to hide. And then *he* stab her. I watch him . . . bram, bram, just so . . . and she scream out and she husband run. I jump up and run to her. I pull out the knife was to see if I could save her, and the blood splatter all over my clothes . . . you never see so much blood . . . and then everybody rush in and hold me. I ain't know how I manage to get away. I tell you is the same man got the police hunting me that kill the woman.'

'Look, man, you want to get out of this island?'

'Yes, yes, yes, . . .'

'Why you don't tell your own brother the truth then?'

'I tell you I ain't kill nobody . . .'

His brother suddenly leapt up and struck him. He fell on to the floor. His brother leaned over him and slapped him back and forth across the face. 'Tell me the TRUTH, boy. I want to hear the TRUTH!'

'What I tell you is the truth, Joe,' he said trying to keep the panic out of his voice, the panic that kept hammering at his brain. 'I ain't kill no woman.'

His brother hit him again. And again. He opened his mouth to make another anguished protest, but he saw his brother's eyes, and the denial froze on his lips.

'All right, Joe,' he sobbed, 'I killed her, only I didn't mean to. I kill her. You satisfied? You going give me a break . . . ?'

They walked along the beach, their eyes darting from side to side with the fear of discovery in their minds.

'How far the boat-shed is from here?' Franklyn asked.

His brother pointed to an iron-corrugated roof among the trees. 'Is here I keep my boat.'

'Other people does use it?'

'Nobody there now. They fishing. I only stay home 'cause Sheila so sick. I wish I had the money to buy the medicine for her . . .'

'I sorry, man, I wish I had some to give you.'

'All these years you t'iefing and yet you poor like me.'

'Is life.'

'You even worse off now. You is a murderer too.'

Franklyn said nothing, but he was full of hurt when he saw his brother look at him that way.

Silence. And Joe was thinking again: suppose the police come to question me! After all, I am his brother, and the police will surely come. I don't want to get into serious trouble like that. And my wife, perhaps dying, and my children starving.

And Franklyn was thinking: What sort of chance I got, with three thousand dollars on my head. Is a wonder nobody ain't recognize me so far . . .

'This is the shed,' Joe said at last. The boathouse was dark and gloomy inside as they entered. 'The fishing boat there,' Joe said. 'It old but it can get us where we going. Wait there now till I come back. I got to make sure everything clear.'

'O.K. Joe. Thanks for doing this for me.'

Joe didn't answer. He looked at Franklyn for a moment and shook his head slowly. Then he walked out into the sunlight and down the beaten path that led to the village. After he was gone Franklyn shut the door securely and sat down to await his return.

Joe was gone a long time. When finally Franklyn heard a knock, he was relieved, but cautious. He waited until he heard Joe's voice call 'Franklyn!'

Franklyn unbolted the door.

And then they were upon him and he went down under a mass of uniforms and clubs, screaming and struggling, as they pinioned his arms and dragged him roughly to his feet.

He snarled like a wild animal, and over the heads of the police in the doorway he saw his brother, his brother who had betrayed him. And, as he strove to get to him, shrieking out curses, someone hit him across the mouth, and they dragged him out into the open, and towards the waiting van.

The Wasteland
Alan Paton

The moment that the bus moved on he knew he was in danger, for by the lights of it he saw the figures of the young men waiting under the tree. That was the thing feared by all, to be waited for by the young men. It was a thing he had talked about, now he was to see it for himself.

It was too late to run after the bus; it went down the dark street like an island of safety in a sea of perils. Though he had known of his danger only for a second, his mouth was already dry, his heart was pounding in his breast, something within him was crying out in protest against the coming event.

His wages were in his purse, he could feel them weighing heavily against his thigh. That was what they wanted from him. Nothing counted against that. His wife could be made a widow, his children made fatherless, nothing counted against that. Mercy was the unknown word.

While he stood there irresolute he heard the young men walking towards him, not only from the side where he had seen them, but from the other also. They did not speak, their intention was unspeakable. The sound of their feet came on the wind to him. The place was well chosen, for behind him was the high wall of the convent, and the barred door that would not open before a man was dead. On the other side of the road was the wasteland, full of wire and iron and the bodies of old cars. It was his only hope, and he moved towards it; as he did so he knew from the whistle that the young men were there too.

His fear was great and instant, and the smell of it went from his body to his nostrils. At that very moment one of them spoke, giving directions. So trapped was he that he was filled suddenly with strength and anger, and he ran towards the wasteland swinging his heavy stick. In the darkness a form loomed up at him, and he swung the stick at it, and heard it give a faint cry of pain. Then he plunged blindly into the wilderness of wire and iron and the bodies of old cars.

Something caught him by the leg, and he brought his stick crashing down on it, but it was no man, only some knife-edged piece of iron. He was sobbing and out of breath, but he pushed on into the waste, while behind him they pushed on also, knocking against the old iron bodies and kicking against tins and buckets. He fell into some grotesque shape of wire; it was barbed and tore at his clothes and flesh. Then it held him, so that it seemed to him that death must be near, and having no other hope, he cried out, 'Help me, help me!' in what should have been a great voice but was voiceless and gasping. He tore at the wire, and it tore at him too, ripping his face and his hands.

Then suddenly he was free. He saw the bus returning, and he cried out again in the great voiceless voice, 'Help me, help me!' Against the lights of it he could plainly see the form of one of the young men. Death was near him, and for a moment he was filled with the injustice of life, that could end thus for one who had always been hard-working and law-abiding. He lifted the heavy stick and brought it down on the head of his pursuer, so that the man crumpled to the ground, moaning and groaning as though life had been unjust to him also.

Then he turned and began to run again, but ran first into the side of an old lorry which sent him reeling. He lay there for a moment expecting the blow that would end him, but even then his wits came back to him, and he turned over twice and was under the lorry. His very entrails seemed to be coming into his mouth, and his lips could taste sweat and blood. His heart was like a wild thing in his breast, and seemed to lift his whole body each time that it beat. He tried to calm it down, thinking it might be heard, and tried to control the noise of his gasping breath, but he could not do either of these things.

Then suddenly against the dark sky he saw two of the young men. He thought they must hear him; but they themselves were gasping like drowned men, and their speech came by fits and starts.

Then one of them said, 'Do you hear?'

They were silent except for their gasping, listening. And he listened also, but could hear nothing but his own exhausted heart.

'I heard a man . . . running . . . on the road,' said one. 'He's got away . . . let's go.'

Then some more of the young men came up, gasping and cursing the man who had got away.

'Freddy,' said one, 'your father's got away.'

But there was no reply.

'Where's Freddy?' one asked.

One said, 'Quiet!' Then he called in a loud voice, 'Freddy.'

But still there was no reply.

'Let's go,' he said.

They moved off slowly and carefully, then one of them stopped.

'We are saved,' he said. 'Here is the man.'

He knelt down on the ground and then fell to cursing.

'There's no money here,' he said.

One of them lit a match, and in the small light of it the man under the lorry saw him fall back.

'It's Freddy,' one said. 'He's dead.'

Then the one who had said 'Quiet' spoke again.

'Lift him up,' he said. 'Put him under the lorry.'

The man under the lorry heard them struggling with the body of the dead young man, and he turned once, twice, deeper into his hiding-place. The young men lifted the body and swung it under the lorry so that it touched him. Then he heard them moving away, not speaking, slowly and quietly, making an occasional sound against some obstruction in the waste.

He turned on his side, so that he would not need to touch the body of the young man. He buried his face in his arms, and said to himself in the **idiom** of his own language, 'People arise! The world is dead.' Then he arose himself, and went heavily out of the wasteland.

idiom: dialect

The Princess Who Stood On Her Own Two Feet

Jeanne Desy

A long time ago in a kingdom by the sea there lived a Princess tall and bright as a sunflower. Whatever the royal tutors taught her, she mastered with ease. She could tally the royal treasure on her gold and silver abacus, and charm even the Wizard with her enchantments. In short, she had every gift but love, for in all the kingdom there was no suitable match for her.

So she played the zither and designed great tapestries and trained her finches to eat from her hand, for she had a way with animals.

Yet she was bored and lonely, as princesses often are, being a breed apart. Seeing her situation, the Wizard came to see her one day, a strange and elegant creature trotting along at his heels. The Princess clapped her hands in delight, for she loved anything odd.

'What is it?' she cried. The Wizard grimaced.

'Who knows?' he said. 'It's supposed to be something enchanted. I got it through the mail.' The Royal Wizard looked a little shamefaced. It was not the first time he had been taken in by mail-order promises.

'It won't turn into anything else,' he explained. 'It just is what it is.'

'But what is it?'

'They call it a dog,' the Wizard said. 'An Afghan hound.'

Since in this kingdom dogs had never been seen, the Princess was quite delighted. When she brushed the silky, golden dog, she secretly thought it looked rather like her, with its thin aristocratic features and delicate nose. Actually, the Wizard had thought so too, but you can never be sure what a Princess will take as an insult. In any case, the Princess and the dog became constant companions. It followed her on her morning rides and slept at the foot of her bed every night. When she talked, it watched her so attentively that she often thought it understood.

Still, a dog is a dog and not a Prince, and the Princess longed to marry. Often she sat at her window in the high tower, her embroidery idle in her aristocratic hands, and gazed down the road, dreaming of a handsome prince in flashing armour.

One summer day word came that the Prince of a neighbouring kingdom wished to discuss an alliance. The royal maids confided that he was dashing and princely, and the Princess's heart leaped with joy. Eagerly she awaited the betrothal feast.

When the Prince entered the great banquet hall and cast his dark, romantic gaze upon her, the Princess nearly swooned in her chair. She sat shyly while everyone toasted the Prince and the golden Princess and peace forever between the two kingdoms. The dog watched quietly from its accustomed place at her feet.

After many leisurely courses, the great feast ended, and the troubadours began to play. The Prince and Princess listened to the lyrical songs honouring their love, and she let him hold her hand under the table – an act noted with triumphant approval by the King and Queen. The Princess was filled with happiness that such a man would love her.

At last the troubadours swung into a waltz, and it was time for the Prince and Princess to lead the dance. Her heart bursting with joy, the Princess rose to take his arm. But as she rose to her feet, a great shadow darkened the Prince's face, and he stared at her as if stricken.

'What is it?' she cried. But the Prince would not speak, and dashed from the hall.

For a long time the Princess studied her mirror that night, wondering what the Prince had seen.

'If you could talk,' she said to the dog, 'you could tell me, I know it,' for the animal's eyes were bright and intelligent. 'What did I do wrong?'

The dog, in fact, *could* talk; it's just that nobody had ever asked him anything before.

'You didn't do anything,' he said. 'It's your height.'

'My height?' The Princess was more astonished by what the dog said rather than the fact that he said it. As an amateur wizard, she had heard of talking animals.

'But I am a Princess!' she wailed. 'I'm supposed to be tall.' For in her kingdom, all the royal family was tall, and the Princess the tallest of all, and she had thought that was the way things were supposed to be.

The dog privately marvelled at her naiveté, and explained that in the world outside this kingdom, men liked to be taller than their wives.

'But why?' asked the Princess.

The dog struggled to explain. 'They think if they're not, they can't . . . train falcons as well. Or something.' Now that he thought for a moment, he didn't know either.

'It's my legs,' she muttered. 'When we were sitting down, everything was fine. It's these darn long legs.' The dog cocked his head. He thought she had nice legs, and he was in a position to know. The Princess strode to the bell pull and summoned the Wizard.

'Okay,' she said when he arrived. 'I know the truth.'

'Who told you?' the Wizard asked. Somebody was in for a bit of a stay in irons.

'The dog.' The Wizard sighed. In fact, he had *known* the creature was enchanted.

'It's my height,' she continued bitterly. The Wizard nodded. 'I want you to make me shorter,' she said. 'A foot shorter, at least. Now.'

Using all his persuasive powers, which were considerable, the Wizard explained to her that he could not possibly do that. 'Fatter,' he said 'yes. Thinner, yes.

Turn you into a raven, maybe. But shorter, no. I cannot make you even an inch shorter, my dear.'

The Princess was inconsolable.

Seeing her sorrow, the King sent his emissary to the neighbouring kingdom with some very attractive offers. Finally the neighbouring King and Queen agreed to persuade the Prince to give the match another chance. The Queen spoke to him grandly of chivalry and honour, and the King spoke to him privately of certain gambling debts.

In due course he arrived at the castle, where the Princess had taken to her canopied bed. They had a lovely romantic talk, with him at her bedside holding her hand, and the nobility, of course, standing respectfully at the foot of the bed, as such things are done. In truth, he found the Princess quite lovely when she was sitting or lying down.

'Come on,' he said, 'let's get some fresh air. We'll go riding.'

He had in mind a certain dragon in these parts, against whom he might display his talents. And so the Prince strode and the Princess slouched to the stables.

On a horse, as in a chair, the Princess was no taller than he, so they cantered along happily. Seeing an attractive hedge ahead, the Prince urged his mount into a gallop and sailed the hedge proudly. He turned to see her appreciation, only to find the Princess doing the same, and holding her seat quite gracefully. Truthfully, he felt like leaving again.

'Didn't anyone ever tell you,' he said coldly, 'that ladies ride side-saddle?' Well of course they had, but the Princess always thought that that was a silly, unbalanced position that took all the fun out of riding. Now she apologised prettily and swung her legs around.

At length the Prince hurdled another fence, even more dashingly than before, and turned to see the Princess attempting to do the same thing. But riding side-saddle, she did not have a sure seat, and tumbled to the ground.

'Girls shouldn't jump,' the Prince told the air, as he helped her up.

But on her feet, she was again a head taller than he. She saw the dim displeasure in his eyes. Then, with truly royal impulsiveness, she made a decision to sacrifice for love. She crumpled to the ground.

'My legs,' she said. 'I can't stand.' The Prince swelled with pride, picked her up, and carried her back to the castle.

There the Royal Physician, the Wizard, and even the Witch examined her legs, with the nobility in attendance.

She was given infusions and teas and herbs and packs, but nothing worked. She simply could not stand.

'When there is nothing wrong but foolishness,' the Witch muttered, 'you can't fix it.' And she left. She had no patience with lovesickness.

The Prince lingered on day after day, as a guest of the King, while the Princess grew well and happy, although she did not stand. Carried to the window seat, she would sit happily and watch him stride around the room, describing his chivalric exploits, and she would smile with contentment. The loss of the use of her legs seemed a small price to pay for such a man. The dog observed her without comment.

Since she was often idle now, the Princess practised witty and amusing sayings. She meant only to please the Prince, but he turned on her after one particularly subtle and clever remark and said sharply, 'Haven't you ever heard that women should be seen and not heard?'

The Princess sank into thought. She didn't quite understand the saying, but she sensed that it was somehow like her tallness. For just as he preferred her sitting, not standing, he seemed more pleased when she listened, and more remote when she talked.

The next day when the Prince came to her chambers he found the royal entourage gathered around her bed.

'What's the matter?' he asked. They told him the Princess could not speak, not for herbs or infusions or magic spells. And the Prince sat by the bed and held her hand and spoke to her gently, and she was given a slate to write her desires. All went well for several days. But the Prince was not a great reader, so she put the slate aside, and made conversation with only her eyes and her smile. The Prince told her daily how lovely she was, and then he occupied himself with princely pastimes. Much of the time her only companion was the dog.

One morning the Prince came to see her before he went hunting. His eyes fixed with disgust on the dog, who lay comfortably over her feet.

'Really,' the Prince said, 'sometimes you surprise me.' He went to strike the dog from the bed, but the Princess stayed his hand. He looked at her in amazement.

That night the princess lay sleepless in the moonlight, and at last, hearing the castle fall silent, and knowing that nobody would catch her talking, she whispered to the dog, 'I don't know what I would do without you.'

'You'd better get used to the idea,' said the dog. 'The Prince doesn't like me.'

'He will never take you away.' The Princess hugged the dog fiercely. The dog looked at her sceptically and gave a little doggy cough.

'He took everything else away,' he said.

'No,' she said. 'I did that. I made myself . . . someone he could love.'

'I love you, too,' the dog said.

'Of course you do.' She scratched his ears.

'And,' said the dog, 'I loved you *then*.' The princess lay a long time thinking before she finally slept.

Then next morning the Prince strode in more handsome and dashing than ever, although, oddly enough, the Princess could have sworn he was getting shorter.

As he leaned down to kiss her, his smile disappeared. She frowned a question at him: What's the matter?

'You've still *got* that thing,' he said, pointing to the dog. The Princess grabbed for her slate.

'He is all I have,' she wrote hastily. The lady-in-waiting read it to the Prince.

'You have *me*,' the Prince said, his chin high. 'I believe you love that smelly thing more than you love me.' He strode (he never walked any other way) to the door.

'I *was* going to talk to you about the wedding feast,' he said, as he left. 'But now, never mind!'

The Princess wept softly and copiously, and the dog licked a tear from her trembling hand.

'What does he *want?*' she asked the dog.

'Roast dog for the wedding feast, I'd imagine,' he said. The Princess cried out in horror.

'Oh, not literally,' the dog said. 'But it follows.' And he would say no more.

At last the Princess called the Wizard and wrote on her slate what the dog had said. The Wizard sighed. How awkward. Talking animals were always so frank. He hemmed and hawed until the Princess glared to remind him that wizards are paid by royalty to advise and interpret – not to sigh.

'All right,' he said at last. 'Things always come in threes. Everything.'

The Princess looked at him blankly.

'Wishes always come in threes,' the Wizard said. 'And sacrifices, too. So far, you've given up walking. You've given up speech. One more to go.'

'Why does he want me to give up the dog?' she wrote.

The Wizard looked sorrowfully at her from under his bushy brows. 'Because you love it,' he said.

'But that takes nothing from him!' she scribbled. The Wizard smiled, thinking that the same thing could be said of her height and her speech.

'If you could convince him of that, my dear,' he said, 'you would be more skilled in magic than I.'

When he was gone, the Princess reached for her cards and cast her own fortune, muttering to herself. The dog watched bright-eyed as the wands of growth were covered by the swords of discord. When the ace of swords fell, the Princess gasped. The dog put a delicate paw on the card.

'You poor dumb thing,' she said, for it is hard to think

of a dog any other way, whether it talks or not. 'You don't understand. That is death on a horse. Death to my love.'

'His banner is the white rose,' said the dog, looking at the card intently. 'He is also rebirth.' They heard the Prince's striding step outside the door.

'Quick,' the Princess said. 'Under the bed.' The dog's large brown eyes spoke volumes, but he flattened and slid under the bed. And the Prince's visit was surprisingly jolly.

After some time the Prince looked around with imitation surprise. 'Something's missing,' he said. 'I know. It's that creature of yours. You know, I think I was allergic to it. I feel much better now that it's gone.' He thumped his chest to show how clear it was. The Princess grabbed her slate, wrote furiously, and thrust it at the Royal Physician.

'"He loved me,"' the Royal Physician read aloud.

'Not as I love you,' the Prince said earnestly. The Princess gestured impatiently for the reading to continue.

'That's not all she wrote,' the Royal Physician said. 'It says "The dog loved me then."'

When everyone was gone, the dog crept out to find the Princess installed at her window seat thinking furiously.

'If I am to keep you,' she said to him, 'we shall have to disenchant you with the spells book.' The dog smiled, or seemed to. She cast dice, she drew pentigrams, she crossed rowan twigs and chanted every incantation in the index. Nothing worked. The dog was still a dog, silken, elegant, and seeming to grin in the heat. Finally the Princess clapped shut the last book and sank back.

'Nothing works,' she said. 'I don't know what we shall do. Meanwhile, when you hear anyone coming, hide in the cupboard or beneath the bed.'

'You're putting off the inevitable,' the dog told her sadly.

'I'll think of something,' she said. But she couldn't.

At last it was the eve of her wedding day. While the rest

of the castle buzzed with excitement, the Princess sat mute in her despair.

'I can't give you up and I can't take you!' she wailed. And her dog saw that she was feeling grave pain.

'Sometimes,' the dog said, looking beyond her shoulder, 'sometimes one must give up everything for love.' The Princess's lip trembled and she looked away.

'What will I *do*?' she cried again. The dog did not answer. She turned toward him and then fell to her knees in shock, for the dog lay motionless on the floor. For hours she sat weeping at his side, holding his lifeless paw.

At last she went to her cupboard and took out her wedding dress, which was of the softest whitest velvet. She wrapped the dog in its folds and picked him up gently.

Through the halls of the castle the Princess walked, and the nobility and chambermaids and royal bishops stopped in their busy preparations to watch her, for the Princess had not walked now for many months. To their astonished faces she said, 'I am going to bury the one who really loved me.'

On the steps of the castle she met the Prince, who was just dismounting and calling out jovial hearty things to his companions. So surprised was he to see her walking that he lost his footing and tumbled to the ground. She paused briefly to look down at him, held the dog closer to her body, and walked on. The Prince got up and went after her.

'What's going on here?' he asked. 'What are you doing? Isn't that your wedding dress?' She turned so he could see the dog's head where it nestled in her left arm.

'I thought you got rid of that thing weeks ago,' the Prince said.

It was difficult for him to find an emotion suitable to this complex situation. He tried feeling hurt.

'What you call "this thing,"' the Princess said, 'died to spare me pain. And I intend to bury him with honour.'

The Prince only half heard her, for he was struck by another realisation.

'You're talking!'

'Yes.' She smiled.

Looking down at him, she said, 'I'm talking. The better to tell you good-bye. So good-bye.' And off she went. She could stride too, when she wanted to.

'Well, my dear,' the Queen said that night, when the Princess appeared in the throne room. 'You've made a proper mess of things. We have alliances to think of. I'm sure you're aware of the very complex negotiations you have quite ruined. Your duty as a Princess . . .'

'It is not necessarily my duty to sacrifice everything,' the Princess interrupted. 'And I have other duties: a Princess says what she thinks. A Princess stands on her own two feet. A Princess stands tall. And she does not betray those who love her.' Her royal parents did not reply. But they seemed to ponder her words.

The Princess lay awake that night for many hours. She was tired from the day's exertions, for she let no other hand dig the dog's grave or fill it, but she could not sleep without the warm weight of the dog across her feet, and the sound of his gentle breathing. At last she put on her cloak and slippers and stole through the silent castle out to the gravesite. There she mused upon love, and what she had given for love, and what the dog had given.

'How foolish we are,' she said aloud. 'For a stupid Prince I let my wise companion die.'

At last the Princess dried her tears on her hem and stirred herself to examine the white rose she had planted on the dog's grave. She watered it again with her little silver watering can. It looked as though it would live.

As she slipped to the castle through the ornamental gardens, she heard a quiet jingling near the gate. On the bridge there was silhouetted a horseman. The delicate silver bridles of his horse sparkled in the moonlight. She could see by his crested shield that he must be nobility, perhaps a Prince. Well, there was many an empty room in the castle tonight, with the wedding feast cancelled and all the guests gone home. She approached the rider.

He was quite an attractive fellow, thin with silky golden hair. She smiled up at him, admiring his lean and elegant hand on the reins.

'Where have you come from?' she asked.

He looked puzzled. 'Truthfully,' he replied, 'I can't remember. I know I have travelled a long dark road, but that is all I know.' He gave an odd little cough.

The Princess looked past him, where the road was bright in the moonlight.

'I see,' she said slowly. 'And what is your banner?' For she could not quite decipher it waving above him. He moved it down. A white rose on a black background.

'Death,' she breathed.

'No, no,' he said, smiling. 'Rebirth. And for that, a death is sometimes necessary.' He dismounted and bent to kiss the Princess's hand. She breathed a tiny prayer as he straightened up, but it was not answered. Indeed, he was several inches shorter than she was. The Princess straightened her spine.

'It is a pleasure to look up to a proud and beautiful lady,' the young Prince said, and his large brown eyes spoke volumes. The Princess blushed.

'We're still holding hands,' she said foolishly. The elegant Prince smiled, and kept hold of her hand, and they went toward the castle.

In the shadows the Wizard watched them benignly until they were out of sight. Then he turned to the fluffy black cat at his feet.

'Well, Mirabelle,' he said. 'One never knows the ways of enchantments.' The cat left off from licking one shoulder for a moment and regarded him, but said nothing. Mirabelle never had been much of a conversationalist.

'Ah, well,' the Wizard said. 'I gather from all this – I shall make a note – that sometimes one must sacrifice for love.'

Mirabelle looked intently at the Wizard. 'On the other hand,' the cat said at last, 'sometimes one must refuse to sacrifice.'

'Worth saying,' said the Wizard approvingly. 'And true. True.'

And then, because he had a weakness for talking animals, he took Mirabelle home for an extra dish of cream.

The Moonpath
Robert Swindells

If the world were flat, and if you could look straight into the rising sun, you would see the land where Nick and Bruin lived. It was a land of sticky days and breathless nights, where the sun came up like an enemy and the wind had flies in it.

At the edge of this land, where bitter waves met hot sand, there lay a town of flat, ugly buildings and narrow streets and in one of these streets stood a blacksmith's forge.

Nick was apprenticed to the blacksmith. All day in his stiff leather apron he worked by the stinging-hot furnace; pumping the bellows or carrying bars of iron for his master. At night he lay on the dusty floor with a chain on his foot. Nick's mother and father had sold him to the blacksmith for seven years. Nick cried for them sometimes, in the night, but he hated them too, and vowed they would never see him again.

Sometimes Nick's master loaded the things he had made on to a handcart, and Nick pulled it through the town to the customer's homes. As he went along, Nick would search the faces of the people he passed. He always hoped for a smile, or a kindly word, but he never found one. It was a mean, ugly town full of mean, ugly people.

One afternoon as he was hauling the cart across the town he saw that a small crowd had gathered in the square. There were shouts, and some laughter. Nick left the cart and went over to look. He was small and thin, and easily slipped through to the front. In the middle of the crowd, on a small patch of beaten dust, stood a bear. There was a collar round its neck with a chain. A man held the chain in one hand and a stick in the other. As Nick watched, the man poked the bear with the stick and cried, 'Down, Bruin!' The bear's legs collapsed and it rolled over in the dust and lay still, playing dead. The people laughed. Somebody dropped a coin in the man's hat. 'Up Bruin!' cried the man, and he jerked on the chain. The bear clambered slowly to its feet. Nick wondered what it felt like to have a coat of thick fur on such a day as this.

The man jabbed his stick into the bear's side. 'Dance, Bruin!' he snarled.

The bear lifted its forepaws and began a slow shuffle on its hind feet, swinging its great head from side to side.

'Faster!' cried the man, and he struck the creature across its paws.

The people laughed. Bruin tried to move a little faster. There was a cloud of flies round its head; they settled near its eyes.

The man put down the stick and produced a battered mouth-organ. He sucked and blew a scratchy tune, and a few more coins fell into the hat. Bruin moved heavily to the thin music. After a while the man stopped playing and the bear dropped onto all four feet. People clapped a little. The man bowed and grinned.

Nick was turning sadly away when the bear raised its head and looked at him. The boy paused, gazing back into those tiny, pain-filled eyes. In that instant, Nick felt something that made his own eyes brim, and caused him to clamp his teeth into his bottom lip. He turned and began to push his way through the crowd. He felt the bear's eyes following him and he could scarcely see through the tears in his own. He lifted the handles of his cart and went on without looking back.

That night, lying on the dusty floor with a chain on his foot, Nick thought about Bruin. He saw the fly-tortured eyes and the dry, lolling tongue and he murmured softly into the dark, 'Some day, Bruin, we will leave this place, you and I. We will sail away to a land that is white and cold as the moon. There will be no flies there, and no chains.' He moved a little and his chain made a clinking sound. He sighed, and closed his eyes. 'One day,' he murmured, and then he slept, while the cold white moon slid silent down the sky.

The next morning his master said, 'Take this boat-hook to Caspar, the fisherman. You will find him on the sand, mending his nets.'

When he stepped out of the forge the sun hit him and he screwed up his eyes. 'This land is an anvil,' he told himself. 'The sun is a great hammer, and it will beat me on the anvil until I am bent and blackened like the end of this boat-hook.' He wiped the sweat from his forehead and turned towards the sea.

Caspar was sitting cross-legged in the sand, mending a net. He looked up, squinting into the sun. 'Ah, my new boat-hook is ready, yes? Give it here.'

Nick handed it to him and stood wiggling his toes in the hot sand.

The fisherman examined the boat-hook and said, 'Tell your master I am satisfied and will pay him tomorrow.'

Nick bobbed his head, and was turning away when the man said, 'I saw you, yesterday. Watching the bear.'

Nick turned. Pale blue eyes regarding him, a twinkle in them somewhere. He nodded. 'Yes. We are both slaves, the bear and I.'

He knew he ought not to have said it. Suppose the man told his master? His eyes, fearful, met Caspar's. The twinkle remained. 'Have no fear,' said the fisherman softly. 'I have no master, but if I had, it would have been the moonpath for me, long ago.'

Nick did not understand. 'The – moonpath?' he whispered.

Caspar nodded.

'What is the moonpath?' asked Nick. Perhaps this man was mocking him.

The fisherman raised his eyebrows. 'The moonpath? Why, the moonpath is the road to freedom; a silver track that lies upon the sea.'

Nick turned, to see warm, brown water moving slug-like in the sun. His lip twisted up. 'I see no silver track,' he said.

Caspar grinned, shaking his head. 'It is not there now, little slave,' he said. His face became grave and he patted the sand beside him. 'Come, sit here and I will tell you.'

Nick approached the man, half-fearful, and sat down. Caspar set aside his net, drew up his knees under his chin, and wrapped his thick arms around them. He gazed out over the sea.

'It is big, the sea,' he said. 'It is the biggest thing on earth, and the fiercest. To cross it you need a good boat.' He glanced sidelong at Nick. 'Slaves do not have boats. But sometimes at night, in the full of the moon, there is a way for them if they believe and are brave.'

Nick waited. After a moment, Caspar nodded towards the sea. 'Out there,' he said, 'when the moon is full, there is a path across the sea. It is long and straight, and at the far end lies a land as cool as this land is hot.' He turned earnest eyes to Nick. 'He who takes the silver path must travel quickly, for it melts with the dawn and is no more until the moon is full again.'

The boy felt a lump in his throat and he gazed at Caspar through tear-filled eyes. 'I have seen such a path,' he choked. 'It is made from light. No one can walk upon it. You mock me.'

Caspar shrugged. 'I told you. A man must believe, and be brave.' He took up a net and began to work upon it as though Nick were no longer there.

After a while the boy blinked away his tears, got up, and walked towards the town.

Many days passed. One evening, at the end of a very hard day, Nick's master beat him and left him waterless. Nick lay a long time crying in the dust. When he had cried all his tears, he sat up and rubbed his eyes with the heels of his hands so that the dust from them made a grey paste on his cheeks.

'I will not stay here,' he told himself, 'to be beaten and starved and roasted. I will run away. I will go tonight.' And he crawled across the floor to where his master had left a large file. His chain was barely long enough, but by lying at full stretch he was able to get his finger-tips to it. He laid the blade across a link and, working rapidly, began to saw at the iron.

An hour he worked, then rested, gasping. He blinked away the sweat and went on. At midnight the link parted. Nick scrambled to his feet and stood, listening. The moon-washed streets were silent.

He left the forge on tiptoe, flitting from shadow to shadow along the road. He did not know where he would go. The town was surrounded on three sides by the desert, and on the other by the sea. The desert, then. He must try to cross the desert. He turned up an alley, and cried out in terror. His master came swiftly, crouching, the great hammer drawn back over a brawny shoulder. Nick whirled and fled.

'Runaway!' roared his master behind him.

His voice echoed all across the midnight town. A door was flung open. Then another. Lights moved in windows. People spilled out of houses. Nick swerved and ran on. The people were shouting to one another. His way was blocked. He spun round. Men, strung out across the street behind him, and his master like some squat ape coming with the hammer. He ran left. A figure crouched, spreading huge arms. He spun. There! A clear run. He gasped, pelting along the unguarded alley, and as he ran he cried out, without knowing it, the name of the only other slave he knew. 'Bruin! Bruin! Bruin! . . . '

Breaking clear of the buildings he glanced over his shoulder. His master followed, closer now, his hammer raised high. Nick ran on desperately then stopped, skidding in damp sand. The sea! They had driven him to the sea! He turned, sobbing, and angled along the beach, dodging between huge rocks and leaping over small ones. He could hear the pounding of his master's boots and the rasping of his breath. He threw back his head and ran wild-eyed, mouth agape. He never saw the rock. It struck him below the knees and he went headlong in the sand. He rolled and screamed, flinging up his arms to cover his face. His master raised the great hammer. A cry. The hammer fell, kicking up sand by Nick's head, and then his master reeled, clutching his side.

A shaggy form swayed erect against the moon, snarling. Bruin! The bear turned, a short length of chain swinging at its neck. Nick gazed up at the great head and then beyond, to where the moon hung cool and full in the velvet sky. Cool and full. Caspar! The boy looked seaward, and it was there. 'I believe!' sobbed Nick.

Men were coming, running quiet in the sand. He scrambled to his feet. 'Come, Bruin!' he cried.

The sand sloped gently down, and they ran; not into the surf, but on to rippled silver, cool and hard. 'I believe!' cried Nick, and they moved out across the midnight sea.

And all along the shore the people stood, their mouths open, staring. One stuck out his foot and snatched it back, drenched with moon-white spray. So they stood, all night, gazing out to sea. From time to time someone would shake his head, or mutter something under his breath. And when it was near to dawn, they looked at one another out of the corners of their eyes, and shuffled their feet, and began to drift away in ones or twos. They walked by the blacksmith, who nursed his side by a rock.

And the blacksmith said to one, 'Where is my boy?' and to another, 'What happened?' But they just shook their heads like people in a dream.

And then the bear's master came dangling the broken lock from Bruin's cage. Far, far away, a cooling wind ruffled Nick's hair and Bruin dropped his head to lap the snow.

Activities

Handsel and Gristle **by Michael Rosen**

1 **In pairs**, read aloud the first two pages of this story.
   Divide them up between you as you wish.

   Then pick out about ten words or phrases that show the
   writer playing jokes with the language of fairy tales.
   'Translate' them back into normal English.

   Which of the writer's jokes on words amuse you most?
   Do they all work in the same way?

2 **In small groups**, plan a Michael Rosen version of
   Cinderella OR your own choice of fairy tale.

   Start by making a list of joke names for the main
   characters. (How would the Ugly Sisters and Buttons
   come out?) Then invent joke words for important places
   and objects in the story, e.g. Prince Charming's Palace,
   Cinderella's kitchen, the pumpkin, the mice that turn into
   horses, the glass slipper . . . and so on.

   Between you, write a three- or four-paragraph version of
   your story in Michael Rosen language. If possible, use a
   computer. Type in your individual contributions, then cut
   and paste them together.

3 **As a class**, listen to a selection of completed tales. Vote
   for those which use words in the most original and
   amusing ways.

Getting Dead **by William F Nolan**

1 **In small groups**, share your memories of stories and films about vampires. What sort of things happen in them? Where are they usually set? What atmosphere tends to be built up? Refer to particular vampire stories that have stuck in your mind.

   Then make a grid to show the differences between a typical vampire story and *Getting Dead*, like this:

Ingredients of typical vampire stories: plot, characters, setting, style	Ingredients of *Getting Dead*: plot, characters, setting, style
1	1
2	2

   Use your grid to work out how the writer of *Getting Dead* deliberately **parodies** (or 'sends up') the vampire story genre. Concentrate most on particular uses of language, e.g : 'He'd locked himself out of his castle several times and thrown away the key, figuring if he couldn't get back inside to his casket by sunrise he'd be cooked to a fine black ash.'

2 **By yourself**, imagine that 'Count Arnold Whatever' decides to behave like a normal vampire after his attempts to die have failed.

   Write a *three*-paragraph story of his next adventure. In the first paragraph you should set the scene. In the next the Count ensnares a human victim. The last paragraph ends the story on a particularly nasty note. Use the language of typical vampire stories.

3 **As a class**, listen to your teacher reading a conventional vampire or horror story.

Consider:

- how does the writer build up an impression of fear and horror?

- how successful is the writer in holding your interest throughout?

- how does the *language* of the story compare with that of your own? Is it more or less effective?

If you wish, revise the story you've written in the light of what you have heard.

Many Happy Returns! **by Barbara Griffiths**

1 'The man had a nail through his head'

   In small groups, think of different kinds of story (or 'genres') which might begin with this sentence. Crime? Horror? Mystery? Science fiction? Talk about how the plot of each genre story you choose could develop from this starting point.

   By yourself, write the *opening* of ONE of these genre stories, beginning with the sentence above. Produce one or two paragraphs. Then read aloud to the group what you have written. Group members should say how effective the style and language of each opening are in holding their interest, and *why*.

2 Much of the story is made up of *dialogue* (i.e. conversation).

   In pairs, compare the ways of speaking of Neville, Jan (Mark's mother), and Mr Smarty-pants. How does their conversation bring out their different characters?

Character	Typical way of speaking	What this shows about them
Neville	1 'Wot, no bog paper?' 2 ?	1 ? 2 ?
Jan	1 'Neville ... Stop that at once. NOT in the sand-pit, if you please!' 2 ?	1 ? 2 ?
Mr Smarty-pants	1 'I am about to perform a most peculiated and compuliar trick' 2 ?	1 ? 2 ?

Then **as a class** discuss the points you have come up with. Apart from bringing out character, how does the dialogue help to:

- move the story forward
- build up suspense
- create humour?

3 **By yourself**, draft and write the opening paragraph of a story that starts with ONE of these sentences:

- Inside its coffin, the body opened heavy-lidded eyes and began to stir.

- 'Sorry to bother you,' Lee said to the old woman who peered grumpily round the weather-beaten door of her cottage, 'but I got separated from my friends when the fog came down and I think I'm lost'.

- With no warning, all the lights of the city snapped off, as if a giant switch had been thrown by some unseen hand.

Exchange your paragraphs **with a partner**. Say how effective you find your partner's style and language in **a)** getting the plot under way, and **b)** establishing a suitable atmosphere for the subject. Then write the next section of *their* story.

Continue like this, writing turn by turn, until you have produced a whole story with which you are both satisfied. (It need not be very long: careful choice of language matters more than length.) If possible, write and edit it on a computer.

A Straight Bat **by Roger Holt**

1   **In a small group**, exchange reactions to George,
    Timothy's father, in this story.

    How accurately do the words and phrases below describe
    him? Show what you think by scoring each out of 5,
    where 5 means 'very accurate' and 1 means 'inaccurate'.
    In each case, find one quotation from the text to explain
    your score.

George's character	1 – 5	Quotation
a caring father		
selfish		
happily married		
narrow-minded		
sensitive to Timothy		
a bully		

Then **as a class** compare your ideas with those of other
groups. In your opinion, who is the story's main
character: George or Timothy?

2   **In pairs**, take turns to read aloud the following pieces of
    dialogue by three of the characters. Use what you
    consider to be a suitable tone of voice.

Margaret, Timothy's mother

- 'You'll soon settle in . . . I know that you're
  starting a term or two behind the other boys, but
  you'll catch up in no time . . . You'll enjoy living
  away from home.'

- 'Have a good time, dear . . . We're both very proud
  of you. Please don't disappoint your father.'

Mrs Tarling, the headmaster's wife

- 'So this is Timothy . . . I was wondering what George Banks' son would look like . . . I see you've brought your cricket bat, Timothy. That's a good start. I hope you'll be happy here.'

Timothy

- 'I don't have the bat any more, Daddy.'

- 'A violin . . . I'm having lessons and I'm in the school orchestra.'

- 'Would you like to hear me play it?'

Discuss what these extracts show about the *feelings* of each character at the points where they are spoken.

Choose ONE of the extracts which you think marks a *turning-point* in the story. Then **join up with another pair**. Compare and justify your choice.

3 **As a class**, look at the writer's use of *symbols* in this story.

In literature, a symbol is any object, or image, which represents an idea the writer wants to stand out as important. Often, symbols give you clues about the story's main theme, or themes.

Talk about the importance to this story of:

- the cricket bat

- the violin, and violin music

- the image of 'a straight bat'.

Refer back to particular points in the text where these are described: e.g. 'The bat rested across his knees like an unexploded bomb' (page 21).

Do you think the writer's use of these symbols is effective – or is it heavy-handed?

4 **By yourself**, imagine you are Timothy. Write three entries in your diary describing your first half-term at Yarlet Hall. They are separated by at least one week.

   During this time you receive letters from both your father and mother. Include your reaction to these in what you write, bearing in mind that your diary is *private*.

   The story shows that Timothy changes quite a lot once he is away from home. Reflect these changes in the style and language you use for each diary entry.

The Trout by Sean O'Faolain

1   **In small groups**, choose four sentences from the story
    that suggest something about Julia's attitude to the trout.
    What do they tell you? Show what you think by filling in
    a grid, like this:

References to the trout	What they show about Julia's attitude
1 'It troubled her that the trout was always in the same position: he had no room to turn' [page 27]	she is thinking more and more about the trout – she's worried that it might be trapped and could die
2	

Why do you think it becomes so important to Julia to
free the trout? What are her feelings about doing so at
the end of the story?

2   **In pairs**, re-read the first two paragraphs of the story.
    Then in 25 words write a *purely factual* description of
    The Dark Walk.

    Compare your description with the writer's. What
    impressions of The Dark Walk does he give that your
    version doesn't? How does he convey Julia's *feelings*
    about The Dark Walk by **a)** his choice of language and
    b) his construction of sentences?

3   **As a class**, re-read the passage beginning 'She sat up'
    and ending ' . . . the radiant pointed face laughing
    down at her out of the empty sky' (page 29).

Consider how the following descriptions help create a
strong *atmosphere* for Julia's night-time visit to The Dark
Walk:

- 'The Dark Walk would be full of little scraps of moon.'

- '[she] scuttled along the cool but cruel gravel'

- 'Something alive rustled inside there.'

- '[she] raced, with her teeth ground, out to the other
  end of the tunnel'

- '. . . she came to the cool ooze of the river's bank.'

Is the atmosphere well suited to conveying Julia's feelings
at this point in the story?

4 **By yourself**, write about an occasion when you have
been deeply afraid and/or in danger. Concentrate more
on describing the *setting* than on stating your feelings
directly. Draft and re-draft, preferably on screen, until
you are satisfied that a reader will re-live the experience
with you.

The Flowers **by Alice Walker**

1   **In small groups**, exchange ideas about:

  • what causes Myop to give 'a little yelp of surprise'

  • what has happened to the 'tall man', and why it may have happened

  • why the writer ends her story with 'And the summer was over'

  • why the story is called *The Flowers*.

2   **As a class**, look in detail at the style and language of this story. Consider:

  • What is the *mood* of the first three paragraphs? Pick out two or three descriptions which help to create it.

  • In paragraph 5, how does the writer signal that the mood is about to change? Look carefully at her choice of adjectives.

  • In paragraphs 6 and 7, how does the writer introduce a sense of *shock*? Pick out two sentences where this is particularly strong. How are the sentences constructed?

  • Why does the writer end her story with a one-sentence paragraph?

  The story is very compressed. What do you think the writer gains, or loses, by this?

3   **In pairs**, use a computer to draft and write a poem version of this story.

  There are nine paragraphs. Choose one phrase or sentence from each which you think captures Myop's feelings in it. For instance, your choice for paragraph 1 might be:

  'each day a golden surprise'

Type out *in order* your nine phrases/sentences.

Now link them together to form an unrhymed poem. You can change words, add words, delete words, and edit your text in other ways. Work towards a satisfying shape for the whole poem which reflects your understanding of the story.

The Empty Box **by Johanna Hurwitz**

1   This story is made up of thirteen letters written by five
        people: Mrs Lillian Peacock, Ms Ellen George for
        Natures Wonder Inc, Mr Andrew Peacock, Jason
        Peacock, and Marilyn Pippin for Natures Wonder Inc.
        (Assume that the letters of February 22 and March 7 are
        sent by Ms Ellen George.)

   As a class, choose *one* letter from each writer sent
   before April 1. Make a class grid like the one below to
   show how the *language and tone* of these letters reflect
   their writer's purpose – i.e. the points they want to make
   and their feelings at the time. Do it like this:

Date of letter	Purpose of letter	How language and tone reflect writer's purpose
Lillian Peacock		
Ellen George		
Andrew Peacock		
Jason Peacock		
Marilyn Pippin		

   Comment on the use of *cliché* and *jargon* in the letters
   from Ms George and Marilyn Pippin. Why do you think
   businesses use these kinds of language?

2   **In pairs**, plan two letters of complaint and two replies to
        them. Possible reasons for complaining include:

- a newly-bought CD, computer game or video that proves to be faulty

- a visit to see a band, a show or a sporting fixture which disappointed you

- a nightmare holiday your family bought from a travel company.

Each of you should write a complaint. Then read your partner's letter. Reply to it as if you are the person representing the organisation/business to which it has been sent.

Adapt your language and tone to the purpose of each letter you write.

3 **In small groups**, re-read Jason Peacock's last letter. Notice its date. What evidence is there in it for thinking it's a 'spoof', possibly encouraged by his parents and his friend Allan?

Imagine it is April Fool's Day. Each of you should take ten minutes to plan a 'tall story' to tell the others, beginning 'This has been the best (OR worst) day of my life'.

Listen to each other's stories. Afterwards, award marks for inventiveness, originality, convincing description, and keeping a straight face.

Do You Dance? by Laurence Staig

1 **As a class**, look closely at the opening paragraph of the story. It includes the phrase: 'This was a strange land'. How do the writer's descriptions create an impression of 'strangeness'?

   In the course of your discussion, comment on the following uses of language and their effect on the reader:

   • 'soft, fragile music'

   • 'as the rays bled into the clouds they stained the sky like a wound'

   • 'shimmered in the light'

   • 'as if they were living things waiting to crawl across the landscape'

   • 'almost the dark side of the moon.'

   Think of what happens later in the story. How do these descriptions prepare you for the strange events that follow?

2 **By yourself**, write the opening two paragraphs of a Mystery Story. Choose your own subject. Use words and phrases which create a strong atmosphere.

   Then write your story's *last* paragraph.

   Join up with a partner. Read each other's paragraphs. Tell your partner **a)** what you think happens in the 'missing' section, and **b)** what kind of atmosphere the writing has, and how well it has been built up.

3 **In small groups**, read aloud the passage beginning 'The pipes were everywhere' (page 51) and ending 'With a groan he realized who the shirts had belonged to' (page 53).

   Each of you should choose *two* sentences from this passage which you think are effectively written. Write down a brief explanation of *why*. You might think about the writer's:

- choice of verbs and adjectives

- use of similes

- sentence construction

- use of punctuation.

Take turns to read out what you have written. Say whether you agree with each other's ideas.

4 **By yourself**, complete your partly-written mystery story. Start by rewriting any sentences you now wish to improve. When writing the rest, think all the time about your choice of words and phrases and the effect you want them to have on a reader.

Out of the Everywhere **by Marilyn Watts**

1 Imagine that this story had been printed *without its final sentence*.

Divide your class into two groups. **Group 1** collects evidence that *Out of the Everywhere* is about the arrival on earth of an alien. **Group 2** collects evidence that it describes the birth and early life of a baby.

In finding your evidence, look at both the *subject-matter* and the *language* of the story. Note down what you decide, like this:

Group 1	Group 2
1 'It came in the night' – writer uses the pronoun 'it' as if describing a non-human creature. The verb 'came' suggests the creature has arrived from another world	1 'We caught our breath and stared' – writer uses the pronoun 'we' to refer to the child's family. The verb 'stared' suggests the usual sense of wonder when a baby is born
2 'So it looked at us … out of its wrinkled, wise face' – writer uses the adjectives 'wrinkled' and 'wise', suggesting the creature has an alien appearance and a superior intelligence	2 'So it looked at us … out of its wrinkled, wise face' – new-born babies normally have wrinkled skin, and parents often think they look intelligent beyond their years

When you have finished, hold a **class debate**. Try to persuade the other group to accept your interpretation of the story. Refer throughout to the writer's choice of language.

2 At certain points in this story, the writer uses a sequence of short sentences. Four examples are given below.

- 'Yet it needed help. It needed something to cover it against the coolness. When we brought a blanket, it quietened. And when we held it, it seemed content.'

- 'But it couldn't last. Nothing so strange ever does. Separate beings, distinct races, can never live together as such for long. One must triumph in the end.'

- 'And in a way it lost. The little thing. It had to.'

- 'Not fully. But nearly. Nearly. Because eventually it gave in and acquiesced. It took time.'

As a class, say what effects the writer achieves by this technique. For example: do the sentence-length and punctuation affect the *tone* of the writing? Is the *rhythm* of sentences important to what is being described?

Look again at the third extract above. Would its impact on the reader be different if it had read:

'In a way the little thing lost, as it had to'?

3 **By yourself**, write a story which makes the reader see something ordinary in a completely new light. Choose your own subject.

One way of doing this is to deliberately mislead your reader about the story's genre by your choice of language. There are, however, other ways. . .

The Breadwinner **by Leslie Halward**

1   **In small groups**, re-read the first section of this story
    from the beginning to 'Nothing more was said for about
    five minutes' (page 59).

    What does the passage tell you about the relationship
    between the boy's parents?

    Copy and complete the grid below to show how the
    writer builds up a feeling of *strain* and *tension* before the
    boy comes in.

Aspects of the writer's style	How it creates a sense of strain and tension
Dialogue:	
• 'You'll keep your hands off the money'	shows that the boy's wages are a bone of contention between his parents – they're preparing for a battle over them
• 'It'll pay the rent and buy us a bit of food'	?
• ' "You shut your mouth" said the man, quietly'	shows that the father has no respect for his wife and no sense of responsibility for the family – 'quietly' is sinister, suggesting he can be vicious and cruel
• 'You're nobody here. Understand? Nobody.'	?
• ' "We'll see about that" said the man, leisurely poking the fire'.	?

Descriptions of the characters:	
• 'She looked tired and frequently sighed heavily.'	The mother is worn out by poverty – the boy's wages are her last chance to keep the home together
• '... the woman from time to time looked contemptuously at her husband.'	?
• 'He ignored her ... making a pretence of being profoundly bored.'	The father knows the battle of wills with his wife is going to come to a head when the boy returns – he is determined not to lose it
• 'He had watery blue eyes and a heavy brown moustache, which he sucked occasionally.'	?
Descriptions of the setting:	
• '... the room, though clean, was meanly furnished'	?
• 'The mother had laid the table and was cutting some slices of bread and butter for tea.'	?

Then **as a class** compare your findings. It has been said that in *The Breadwinner* the writer 'doesn't waste a word'. On the evidence of this passage, do you agree?

2 **In pairs**, re-read *aloud* the section of the story from 'Then the boy came in' (page 59) to 'When he had done this he went straight upstairs' (page 60).

Discuss how the writer uses a mixture of dialogue and description to bring out **a)** the father's brutality, and **b)** the boy's bravery. Look closely at particular uses of language: e.g. 'The father advanced on the boy, his teeth showing in a snarl under his big moustache' (page 59).

Here the boy is deliberately lying to his father. Does this reduce your sympathy for him, or add to it?

3 **By yourself**, add a further section to this story showing what happens when the father returns home later in the evening. Decide whether it will include the boy.

Write in a style as near as possible to Leslie Halward's, using some of the techniques you have been examining.

Fabric Crafts **by Anne Fine**

1   **As a class**, discuss briefly what is meant by a 'stereotypical character'. Refer to stories you have read, and TV programmes (especially soaps and sitcoms) you have seen, which feature such stereotypes as:

- the nosy neighbour
- the fussy middle-class housewife
- the tearaway teenager
- the likeable rogue
- the gossipy do-gooder.

Then **in small groups** plan and act out part of an episode of *Neighbours At Home In Coronation Square*. Include at least two stereotypical characters. Bring out clearly **a)** their attitudes to life and **b)** their ways of speaking and the language they use.

2   **In pairs**, find evidence from *Fabric Crafts* that Alastair MacIntyre is a stereotype of an old-fashioned husband and father. Look both at what he says AND the language and tone in which he says it.

Put what you find onto a grid, like this:

Alastair's attitudes	Evidence from the text
1 He thinks his children should be taught only **academic** subjects at school	'What about you, laddie? Are you all packed and ready for a long day in school? Climbing boots? Beekeeping gear? Snorkel and oxygen tank?'
2	[pages 63–4]

Make at least *five* entries on your grid.

Then **join up with another pair**. Compare and explain what you've noted down. Where do you think Alastair's prejudices come from? Is the writer's purpose to make fun of Alastair – or is it to make fun of Blair?

3   **In small groups**, look at how the vocabulary of Fabric Crafts is used in the extracts below. How does it guide your response to boys taking a serious interest in the subject?

- 'I dinnae just chat. I'm very good. I've started on embroidery now I've finished hemming my apron!'

- 'Jimmy and Iain were here already. He sent them along to The Work Box on Pitlochrie Street to buy another skein of Flaming Orange so he could finish off his border of french knots.'

- 'I am watching,' said Blair. 'You should try watching telly and doing satin stitch. It's no' the easiest thing.'

- 'What do you reckon?' he said. 'Be honest. Dinnae spare my feelings. Do ye think those stitches in China Blue are entirely regular? Now look very closely. I want ye to be picky.'

Do you think the writer intends these passages simply to amuse you – or is she also showing that 'The times are changing' (page 64)?

4   **By yourself**, write a monologue for radio or television in which a stereotypical character describes a day (or an important event) in their life. Bring out their personality and attitudes through the language, tone, sentence structure and sentence length they use.

In preparation, it would be helpful to watch a video of one of Alan Bennett's *Talking Heads* monologues, broadcast on BBC TV in the 1990s.

Hobbyist **by Fredric Brown**

1   *Hobbyist* is a crime story with a twist, in which the tables are turned against Sangstrom, the would-be murderer.

In small groups, copy and complete the grid below to show how all Sangstrom's plans are thwarted by the druggist.

What Sangstrom intends to do at various points in the story	How the druggist outwits Sangstrom at various points in the story
1 He wants the druggist to sell him a 'completely undetectable poison' with which to kill his wife 2	1 He puts poison in Sangstrom's coffee to prevent him committing the murder 2

Why do you think the story is entitled *Hobbyist*? Has the title been well-chosen? Refer to details from the text to support your opinion.

2   Much of this story is told through *dialogue* between its only two characters.

As a class, consider why the writer may have chosen to use this narrative device.

Then look at the style and language of the descriptions that come *between* passages of dialogue. Strictly speaking, are these descriptions necessary to the plot? What, if anything, do you think they add to the story?

You could start by examining the following:

• 'The druggist was a gnomelike gnarled little man . . . '

- 'He came around the counter and locked the front door of the shop . . .'

- 'Sangstrom followed him . . . to a back room ringed by shelves of bottles from floor to ceiling.'

3   **By yourself**, write a crime story made up largely of dialogue between the criminal and his/her intended victim. Choose your own situation. It could centre on a robbery, a kidnap, attempted blackmail, etc.

Use description to achieve similar effects to those you examined in *Hobbyist*. Make every word count.

A Price to Pay by Timothy Callender

1 **In small groups**, talk about the way the writer makes you feel towards Franklyn *at different points in the story*.

Find examples of where the descriptions lead you to feel:

- mainly sympathetic to him

- mainly critical of him

- a mixture of feelings about him.

Show what you decide by filling in the grid below.

Feelings towards Franklyn		
A Sympathetic, because: 1 2	B Critical, because: 1 2	C Mixed feelings, because: 1 2

Now choose ONE quotation to illustrate each of the headings **A, B** and **C**. Look carefully at the writer's use of vocabulary, tone and sentence-structure in your three quotations. How do these help to guide your response to Franklyn?

2 **As a class**, read the two paragraphs below describing Franklyn on the run from the police.

He stood up for a moment, and then began to run. His feet moved rhythmically across the sand. He wanted to stop, he was so tired, but he dared not because his pursuers were closing in on him all the time.

He could see the lights of their torches through the trees. He had reached the edge of the sea, so he hoped he was out of their range. However, he soon saw to his right another group of lights. He realised he was surrounded. He heard dogs barking somewhere behind him, but how far away they were he could not tell.

Compare this passage with the two paragraphs Timothy Callender *actually* wrote (page 76). Both passages give the same information. Why, then, does the 'real' passage make a much stronger impression on the reader?

In making your comparison, look closely at how Timothy Callender:

- builds up each paragraph as a unit

- constructs any *two* sentences in such a way that they reflect what they describe

- uses adverbials to link sentences together and maintain the 'flow' of the narrative

- makes use of imagery

- helps the reader experience the situation from Franklyn's viewpoint.

3 **By yourself**, draft two paragraphs from the start of a story describing a serious accident. It can be based on real or imagined experience.

Draft the paragraphs quite quickly to get down on paper the information you want to give.

Then re-draft what you have written. Use some of the writing techniques you examined in Activity 2 to hold the reader's interest and involve them in the story.

The Wasteland **by Alan Paton**

1 **In pairs**, work out exactly what happens in this story. Ask yourselves:

- what do you know about the man whom the gang intends to rob?

- how does the man manage to escape with his life?

- who is Freddy? What happens to him?

- in the last paragraph, why does the man say 'People arise! The world is dead'?

Join up with another pair. Compare your ideas and justify them by referring to the text.

2 **In small groups**, find where the following sentences occur. Re-read them *aloud*.

- 'It was too late to run after the bus; it went down the dark street like an island of safety in a sea of perils.'

- 'His heart was like a wild thing in his breast, and seemed to lift his body each time that it beat.'

- 'The man under the lorry heard them struggling with the body of the dead young man, and he turned once, twice, deeper into his hiding-place.'

How do the style and language of each sentence convey the man's fear? Comment in particular on **a**) the writer's use of *imagery* and **b**) the way the sentences are constructed.

3 The *setting* for most of this story is the wasteland, a 'wilderness of wire and iron and the bodies of old cars' (page 85).

As a class, make a grid to show **a**) how the writer describes what is in the wasteland, and **b**) what *effect* his descriptions have on you. Do it like this:

The writer's descriptions	Their effect on the reader
1 'some knife-edged piece of iron' (page 85)	makes a bit of discarded rubbish seem dangerous and threatening – reflects the man's fear of being attacked by the gang, probably with knives
2	

How much do the descriptions of the wasteland setting add to the story's effect? Why do you think the writer chose *The Wasteland* as his title?

4   **By yourself**, think of an experience you have had where you felt one of these emotions very strongly:

- anxiety
- excitement
- anger
- boredom
- terror
- contentment

Bring to mind the *setting* or place you associate with the feeling you have chosen. Write a page describing this setting without making direct reference to the feeling you had there.

Then exchange your writing **with a partner**. Can your partner work out what you were feeling at this time? If so, how?

The Princess Who Stood On Her Own Two Feet by Jeanne Desy

1 **In small groups**, find evidence that the first Prince treats the Princess in a *sexist* and insensitive way. Include examples of his use of sexist language. Put your findings onto a grid, like this:

Examples of the Prince's sexist and insensitive behaviour and language	The Princess's reaction to it
1 'Haven't you heard that women should be seen and not heard?' (page 93)	She stops speaking so as not to offend or lose the Prince
2	

List five or six examples. Does the Princess *always* do as the Prince demands?

Then **as a class** exchange ideas about the moral of this story. What part does the Princess's dog play in helping you understand it?

2 **As a class**, look closely at the extracts below. Discuss how their style and language are meant to remind you of traditional fairy tales.

- The opening sentence.

- 'After many leisurely courses, the great feast ended, and the troubadours began to play. The Prince and Princess listened to the lyrical songs honouring their love, and she let him hold her hand under the table.' (page 89)

- 'She was given infusions and teas and herbs and packs, but nothing worked. She simply could not stand. "When there is nothing wrong but foolishness," the Witch muttered, "you can't fix it". And she left' (page 93).

- 'As she slipped to the castle through the ornamental gardens, she heard a quiet jingling near the gate. On the bridge there was silhouetted a horseman. The delicate silver bridles of his horse sparkled in the moonlight' (page 98).

- '"It is a pleasure to look up to a proud and beautiful lady," the young Prince said, and his large brown eyes spoke volumes. The Princess blushed. "We're still holding hands," she said foolishly' (page 99).

Which details of language in these extracts, and in other parts of the story, strike you as being *modern*? What purpose is served by mixing together traditional and modern styles?

3   Fairy tales often make use of *symbols* to convey their meaning. For example: the thorn from a beautiful rose which draws blood could stand for the pains, as well as the pleasures, of love.

In pairs, consider the following symbols in *The Princess Who Stood On Her Two Feet*. Say what you think they might stand for, bearing in mind the story as a whole.

- the slate on which the Princess 'speaks' to the Prince

- the ace of swords which the Princess turns up when she tells her own fortune

- the white rose which the Princess plants on her dog's grave

- the emblem on the young Prince's banner: a white rose against a black background.

Are there any other symbols you have picked out while reading? If so, consider their meaning and the part they play in the story.

4 **By yourself**, write a modern fairy tale in a similar style to Jeanne Desy's.

Choose your own plot, characters and theme OR write an up-to-date version of a fairy tale you already know well.

The Moonpath **by Robert Swindells**

1   **As a class**, re-read the paragraph on page 105 beginning 'His voice echoed all across the midnight town'. What point has the story reached here?

In this paragraph there are 17 sentences. Many of them are very short. Some are deliberately ungrammatical (which ones?).

Talk about why the writer has chosen to build up the paragraph in the way he has. Do you find his style effective for what is being described?

2   **By yourself**, plan one or two paragraphs from a story describing someone being chased, either on foot or in a vehicle. Choose your own situation and setting.

If possible, draft it on a computer. You could start by making a list of *verbs* you intend to use. Then build sentences around them. Link these together in ways that create a feeling of danger and suspense.

3   **In small groups**, look at the ten extracts from the story printed below.

Five of them describe the town where Nick and Bruin live. Five describe the moonpath and/or the land to which it leads.

- 'This land is an anvil . . . The sun is a great hammer, and it will beat me on the anvil'

- ' . . . a land that is white and cold as the moon'

- ' . . . he worked by the stinging-hot furnace'

- 'There was a cloud of flies round its head; they settled near its eyes'

- 'Why, the moonpath is the road to freedom, a silver track that lies upon the sea'

- ' . . . it melts with the dawn'

- 'It was a land of sticky days and breathless nights'

- ' . . . they ran; not into the surf but on to rippled silver, cool and hard'

- 'He saw the fly-tortured eyes and the dry, lolling tongue'

- ' . . . where the moon hung cool and full in the velvet sky'

Without looking back at the story, group the extracts together in two columns. Make notes on the *contrasting* impressions they give. How does the writer bring out these contrasts? Talk about:

- the use of verbs

- the use of adjectives

- the use of metaphors

- the *sound* of words.

Then **as a class** exchange your ideas. Say how effective you find the writer's way with words, both in these extracts and in other parts of the story.

Using the Collection

The chart opposite has been created to help teachers make full and flexible use of the stories in this book.

For more information and suggestions on using the collection, please see p. vii.

Title	Theme/Genre	to build up excitement or tension	to create and convey character	to establish narrative voice, viewpoint and/or genre	to evoke setting mood and atmosphere
Handsel and Gristle *(page 1)*	Fairy tale parody			✓	
Getting Dead *(page 6)*	Horror story parody	✓	✓	✓	
Many Happy Returns! *(page 12)*	Ghost story		✓		
A Straight Bat *(page 20)*	Growing up (male teenager)		✓	✓	
The Trout *(page 25)*	Growing up (female teenager)	✓	✓		✓
The Flowers *(page 30)*	Growing up (young child)	✓			✓
The Empty Box *(page 32)*	Letters narrative		✓	✓	
Do You Dance? *(page 42)*	Mystery story/Supernatural	✓			✓
Out of the Everywhere *(page 55)*	Mystery story/Science fiction			✓	✓
The Breadwinner *(page 58)*	Family conflict/Gender roles	✓	✓		
Fabric Crafts *(page 62)*	Family conflict/Gender roles		✓	✓	
Hobbyist *(page 73)*	Murder story	✓		✓	
A Price to Pay *(page 76)*	Crime thriller/Family relationships	✓	✓		✓
The Wasteland *(page 84)*	Crime thriller/Family relationships	✓			✓
The Princess Who Stood On Her Own Two Feet *(page 88)*	Modern fable		✓	✓	
The Moonpath *(page 101)*	Modern fable/Allegory	✓			✓

Main functions of language highlighted in the Activities:

Other New Windmills you might enjoy

From Beginning to End
A New Windmill Book of Short Stories
Edited by Mike Royston

Original openings, ingenious endings; experimental forms, innovative structures. This lively collection for Key Stage 3 shows how and why short stories are shaped in a surprising variety of ways.

- *Runaway Kim is cold and wet hitching on he Interstate. When a fast car pulls over, it seems the perfect chance to show her bossy parents that, at 15, she's old enough to take care of herself . . . isn't she?*

- *Fleeing for life from the enemy, Juan finds his way blocked by a steep-sided gulf. A group of mysterious strangers come up with a daring plan to help him across. Who are they – and what are their motives?*

- *Kurt is sure he has got away with murder – until the police recover his stolen car. They have evidence that its driver is the woman he knows he's killed . . .*

The collection includes stories by established authors such as Leon Garfield, Jamila Gavin, Dennis Hamley and Geraldine McCaughrean.

Age 12+   ISBN: 0 435 12535 4

Other New Windmills you might enjoy

From Hereabout Hill
A New Windmill Book of Short Stories
By Michael Morpurgo

This collection includes a wide variety of genres such as ghostly tales, mythological stories and realistic narrative, including:

- **What Does It Feel Like?** – Sofia is late for school when she sees tanks arrive in the village square. She manages to hide, only to witness horrific events.
- **The Owl and the Pussycat** – An abandoned owlet seems to be on the road to recovery when it is rescued and fed. But why is the large ginger cat so interested?
- **Silver Ghost** – A young Canadian comes to Britain to visit his ancestral home. Who is the strange old man he meets at the house and how can he explain to the police the events which follow…?

Each story has an introduction written by Michael Morpurgo himself. He has crafted a thought-provoking and captivating collection, ideal for exploring different narrative styles and viewpoints.

Age 12+   ISBN: 0 435 12528 1

King of Shadows

By Susan Cooper

I sat there gaping at him, trying to cope with the unbelievable, with being bang in the middle of something that was totally impossible. All I could think was: why is this happening to me?

Nathan Field, an American orphan, arrives in London to act in *A Midsummer Night's Dream* at the Globe Theatre. Rehearsals have only just begun when he suddenly falls ill. When he wakes up in a strange world, Nathan's experiences and friendships will change his life for ever.

Shortlisted for the Carnegie Medal

Age 12+   ISBN: 0 435 12538 9

Heinemann
New Windmills

Founding Editors: Anne and Ian Serraillier

Chinua Achebe Things Fall Apart
David Almond Skellig
Maya Angelou I Know Why the Caged Bird Sings
Margaret Atwood The Handmaid's Tale
Jane Austen Pride and Prejudice
J G Ballard Empire of the Sun
Stan Barstow Joby; A Kind of Loving
Nina Bawden Carrie's War; Devil by the Sea; Kept in the Dark; The Finding; Humbug
Lesley Beake A Cageful of Butterflies
Malorie Blackman Tell Me No Lies; Words Last Forever
Ray Bradbury The Golden Apples of the Sun; The Illustrated Man
Betsy Byars The Midnight Fox; The Pinballs; The Not-Just-Anybody Family; The Eighteenth Emergency
Victor Canning The Runaways
Jane Leslie Conly Racso and the Rats of NIMH
Susan Cooper King of Shadows
Robert Cormier We All Fall Down; Heroes
Roald Dahl Danny, The Champion of the World; The Wonderful Story of Henry Sugar; George's Marvellous Medicine; The BFG; The Witches; Boy; Going Solo; Matilda; My Year
Anita Desai The Village by the Sea
Charles Dickens A Christmas Carol; Great Expectations; Hard Times; Oliver Twist; A Charles Dickens Selection
Berlie Doherty Granny was a Buffer Girl; Street Child
Roddy Doyle Paddy Clarke Ha Ha Ha
Anne Fine The Granny Project
Jamila Gavin The Wheel of Surya
Graham Greene The Third Man and The Fallen Idol; Brighton Rock
Thomas Hardy The Withered Arm and Other Wessex Tales
L P Hartley The Go-Between
Ernest Hemmingway The Old Man and the Sea; A Farewell to Arms
Barry Hines A Kestrel For A Knave
Nigel Hinton Getting Free; Buddy; Buddy's Song; Out of the Darkness
Anne Holm I Am David
Janni Howker Badger on the Barge; The Nature of the Beast; Martin Farrell

Pete Johnson The Protectors
Jennifer Johnston Shadows on Our Skin
Geraldine Kaye Comfort Herself
Daniel Keyes Flowers for Algernon
Dick King-Smith The Sheep-Pig
Elizabeth Laird Red Sky in the Morning; Kiss the Dust
D H Lawrence The Fox and The Virgin and the Gypsy; Selected Tales
George Layton The Swap
Harper Lee To Kill a Mockingbird
C Day Lewis The Otterbury Incident
Joan Lingard Across the Barricades; The File on Fraulein Berg
Penelope Lively The Ghost of Thomas Kempe
Jack London The Call of the Wild; White Fang
Bernard MacLaverty Cal; The Best of Bernard Mac Laverty
James Vance Marshall Walkabout
Ian McEwan The Daydreamer; A Child in Time
Michael Morpurgo My Friend Walter; The Wreck of the Zanzibar;
The War of Jenkins' Ear; Why the Whales Came; Arthur, High King
of Britain; Kensuke's Kingdom; Hereabout Hill
Beverley Naidoo No Turning Back
Bill Naughton The Goalkeeper's Revenge
New Windmill A Charles Dickens Selection
New Windmill Book of Classic Short Stories
New Windmill Book of Fiction and Non-fiction: Taking Off!
New Windmill Book of Haunting Tales
New Windmill Book of Humorous Stories: Don't Make Me Laugh
New Windmill Book of Nineteenth Century Short Stories
New Windmill Book of Non-fiction: Get Real!
New Windmill Book of Non-fiction: Real Lives, Real Times
New Windmill Book of Scottish Short Stories
New Windmill Book of Short Stories: Fast and Curious
New Windmill Book of Short Stories: From Beginning to End
New Windmill Book of Short Stories: Into the Unknown
New Windmill Book of Short Stories: Tales with a Twist
New Windmill Book of Short Stories: Trouble in Two Centuries
New Windmill Book of Short Stories: Ways with Words
New Windmill Book of Short Stories by Women
New Windmill Book of Stories from many Cultures and Traditions:
Fifty-Fifty Tutti-Frutti Chocolate-Chip
New Windmill Book of Stories from Many Genres: Myths, Murders
and Mysteries

How many have you read?